Praise for
Ending the Diet Mindset

"In *Ending the Diet Mindset,* Becca Clegg skillfully shows how dieting actually supports the tyranny of food and body obsession, rather than delivering on its promise of freedom from negative body image. Using her own personal recovery experience, in addition to her professional expertise as a certified eating-disorder therapist, she compassionately spells out what diet mentality is—and how to transform it to achieve a peaceful, balanced relationship with food. I highly recommend this book to all those seeking to transform their relationship with food and claim their birthright to live freely and joyfully in their bodies."

—Anita Johnston, PhD
Author, *Eating in the Light of the Moon*

"In *Ending the Dieting Mindset,* Becca Clegg provides a unique and invaluable resource for those stuck in the painful life of the diet. Drawing from personal experience and years of professional work, Becca captures the essence of the Diet Mindset in each of its manifestations and provides practical strategies to directly address both the core beliefs and the behaviors that can follow. Readers, whether they are individuals struggling through the Diet Mindset or clinicians wanting to help clients with these issues, will glean insight and gain tools to move forward in a different way. *Ending the Diet Mindset* has the potential to change the pattern of disordered eating before it becomes an eating disorder."

—Jonathan Levy, MD
Adult, Child, and Adolescent Psychiatrist
Specializing in Eating Disorders

"*Ending the Diet Mindset* is an amazing guide to help people reclaim their relationship with food and body image. The ten mindset shifts are powerfully transformative and helpful to any person who has ever struggled with food, from dieting to eating disorders and anywhere in between. Becca Clegg's insightful tips and strategies can empower anyone to reclaim their relationship with food. This book is the perfect guide to healing. I have used these mindset shifts with clients and achieved noteworthy results. Thank you, Becca, for this helpful tool!"

—Tara Arnold, PhD, LCSW
Certified Eating-Disorder Specialist and Supervisor

"As a consulting dietician, *Ending the Diet Mindset* will be the cornerstone of my practice working with clients with weight and body-image concerns. This book hits all the right notes in describing why restrictive dieting is damaging, providing insight into specific aspects of the diet mentality that will resonate with the reader and laying the groundwork for making peace with food and weight. Becca Clegg gives the reader the privilege of relating her own experiences with dieting, lending credibility to this work, and writes in a manner that is relatable and poignant, with laugh-out-loud moments. Truly inspiring—this book is a true gift. This book will heal a lot of hearts heavy with the burden of carrying unrealistic expectations so they can let go of the cycle of dieting and shift the focus to living a fulfilled, wholehearted life."

—Cindy Heiss, PhD, RDN, LD
Private-Practice/Consulting Dietician, Diabetes Educator, and Nutrition Faculty

"*Ending the Diet Mindset* is like fresh air in the cultural smog of dieting and deprivation messages. Becca Clegg writes in a familiar, accessible voice, balancing research, years of clinical practice, and wisdom from lived experience. She lays out a practical yet soulful approach to help women stop cycles of body shame and dieting. As a couple and sex therapist, I was struck by how many parallels there are between Becca's work to help women find body love and acceptance, and my own work to help individuals and couples heal and celebrate sexuality. Body shame is inherently sexual shame, and vice versa. As we learn to listen more mindfully to ourselves, practice self-compassion, and receive abundantly, we can heal old wounds, relate more deeply, and experience more joy and pleasure. Thank you, Becca, for this gem!"

—Erika Pluhar, PhD, EdS
Clinical Co-Director of WholeHeart Psychotherapy

"This is the book I wish my mom would have handed me when I was fifteen and beginning to struggle with my weight and self-image. *Wise, witty,* and *totally readable* are not words one usually associates with diet books, but Becca Clegg's *Ending the Diet Mindset* is all that and more. If you're ready to shift your relationship with food and find not only a sane way to eat but a sane way to live, this book is for you. You'll learn a whole new approach to losing weight, which will help you understand why your past efforts have left you feeling like a failure. After reading *Ending the Diet Mindset,* you'll recognize how your brain and biology can derail your dieting efforts and you'll understand how to work with your primal psychology to nurture your body toward health and vibrance. This book is a true gift to every woman who has ever failed at dieting or felt uncomfortable in her own body."

—Maia Toll, MA
Folklorist and Women's Wisdom Mentor
Author of *The Illustrated Herbiary*

"When does well-intended self-improvement become self-abuse? It is, strangely, a fine line. Becca Clegg wisely and lovingly leads you on a journey from food being the enemy, to being friends with what's on your fork. Be warned, a side effect of reading this book might also include becoming your own best friend! Becca does a great job of helping the reader see how your relationship with food mirrors your relationship with yourself, with the people you love the most, and with receiving love and joy and well-being. Becca gives readers doable steps to shift out of the negative Diet

Mindsets and into a more compassionate relationship with your body. The world treats you the way you treat you, and this book helps anyone getting in their own way melt the internal barriers they may have to receiving love, ease, joy, and well-being."

—Mika Ross, MEd, LPC, NCC
Therapist and Relationship Coach

"Becca Clegg, LPC, CEDS, has written a dynamic book that demonstrates how she is able to help people stop following restrictive diets that ultimately harm more than they help people. Becca explores different avenues of our culture that cause people to have negative and unhealthy ideas about their bodies and provides strategies on how to stop the body loathing and develop healthier attitudes toward food and body image. Becca does a great job explaining the reason why diets don't work and reminds us that finding foods that provide pleasure is the area we want to focus on. Lastly, Becca emphasizes that it doesn't matter what size you are to have a healthy relationship with food and your body. I would recommend this book to all because it is something that people in our culture badly need to read."

—Robyn L. Goldberg, RDN, CEDRD
Nutrition Therapist
Certified Intuitive-Eating Professional

"Becca Clegg does a great job of providing insightful and memorable examples of why dieting is so destructive. Throughout the book, Becca gives thought-provoking questions and action steps to connect the reader to their inner wisdom on nurturing the body, mind, and soul with satisfying foods. *Ending the Diet Mindset* helps the reader to discover the subconscious processes that undermine our self-worth while we are dieting. I will definitely use her practical approach of ten mindset shifts with professionals and clients in the process of healing diet mentality, disordered eating, and body-image struggles."

—Kathryn Fink Martinez, RD, CEDRD-S
Certified Intuitive-Eating Professional

"A book that every woman can relate to! In my executive coaching practice, I see firsthand how women in leadership roles get bogged down in 'shoulds' and shame around their appearance. For far too long, women have been burning energy focusing on weight and dieting. No more! With the ten Diet Mindsets clearly and cleverly spelled out, Becca Clegg includes easy, actionable steps to overcome and replace those destructive thoughts with new and empowering ones. Finally, women can reclaim their focus and become the leaders they were born to be. Becca is like the best friend you wish you had, who tells you what you need to hear—no matter how difficult—and does it in a way that feels like a hug. Her expertise in food psychology, combined with her own personal experience, lends authenticity and credibility in her work. She and her book are the real deal."

—Barbara Churchill
Master Executive Coach and Leadership-Development Expert

Ending the Diet Mindset

Ending the Diet Mindset

Reclaim a Healthy and Balanced Relationship with Food and Body Image

Becca Clegg, LPC, CEDS

Alpharetta, GA

This book is not intended as a substitute for the medical advice of physicians. The reader should consult a physician regularly in any matters relating to his/her health, particularly with respect to any symptoms or illness that may require diagnosis or medical attention.

ISBN: 978-1-63183-219-2

Library of Congress Control Number: 2018901483

10 9 8 7 6 5 4 3 2 0 2 0 8 1 8

Printed in the United States of America

∞This paper meets the requirements of ANSI/NISO Z39.48-1992 (Permanence of Paper)

For Kitty and Molly, two of the strongest women I've ever known.

"If I have seen further it is only by standing on the shoulders of giants."

—Sir Isaac Newton

Contents

Acknowledgments

I want to thank so many people who directly and indirectly supported me in writing this, my first book. The creative process involved in making this book come to life was one that tested me and required that I practice every last ounce of tolerance, balance, and compassion I so passionately advocate for in the book itself.

Thank you to the wise ones and teachers, many of whom I have referenced in this book, who have come before me and paved the way. Thank you to my colleagues and friends who have guided my practice. Tara, your patient insistence that I publish my writing and the support, accountability, and friendship you have given me during this process is something I will forever be grateful for. To my family, for their continued support of me through my entire journey; I am beyond lucky to have been born into the family I have, and I can't thank you enough for helping in the countless ways I cannot even begin to list. To my husband, Tom. You have supported me without question, in ways that are obvious and many that are not. Just know I am aware of and grateful for all the things you do, big and small, to help me realize my dreams. I couldn't love you more if I tried.

And lastly, I want to take a moment to honor and deeply thank all of my clients, both present and past. I learn as much from you as I hope you learn from me. Watching you move through your pain into your power will never, ever be something I cease to be amazed by. Your courage, fortitude, resilience, and strength are amazing. This book is our book. Thank you for helping me bring this book to life. My hope is that it might help one more woman realize she is capable of living a life free from the inner tyranny of dieting.

Introduction

Had I not created my whole world, I would have certainly died in other people's.

—Anaïs Nin

If you're reading this, chances are you have been on a few diets in your lifetime. That means that you are also all too aware that dieting doesn't work the way it is supposed to. I mean, in a perfect world, you follow the instructions, you get results, and you would be done. Right? Who has ever been on just one diet? No one!

I have had a lot of experience with diets. I am a therapist, and I have spent my career working with women who have struggled with eating and body-image issues. Once upon a time, however, I was also wrapped up in my own unhealthy pattern of diet and weight obsession.

I know from my firsthand experience the destructive effect that dieting and weight obsession can have on your self-esteem. I've been where you are. I know how desperately you want to stop this never-ending cycle. You can't remember the last time you felt at peace with food, and a large part of you just wants to stop struggling.

Dieting is the problem, not the solution it promises to be. Diets cause us to eat more, not less. Dieting leads us to feel terrible about ourselves, belittles our self-worth, decreases our motivation, and harms our bodies in the process. We are all being sold a "product" that not only doesn't work, but it causes the problem it is supposed to solve. All of this will be explained in detail in the book, as my hope is that when you are done reading, you will understand just how destructive dieting truly is for your mind, body, and spirit.

You want to stop thinking about food all the time. You want to go through a day without worrying about gaining, maintaining, or losing weight. You really just want to start living your life free from the tyranny of dieting and weight obsession. Freedom, peace, and a feeling of contentment with who you are and where you are: that is what you really want.

I want to offer you a new way of thinking about how you relate to food and a new experience in which you create a balanced and relaxed relationship with eating. What you are about to read is the collective wisdom of my own personal experiences and the experiences of hundreds of clients who have moved from struggling with food to creating a healthy relationship with feeding, nourishing, and respecting their bodies.

My Story

It was when she first dared to see her truth that the winds howled. After a time, it strengthened her and she spoke her truth and the earth shook. And when finally, she believed her truth—the stars rejoiced, the universe opened, and even her bones sang: "I Matter!"

—Terri St. Cloud

When I was a small girl, I was what someone would probably call chubby. Looking back, I was just a tall and muscular child with baby fat. Oh, if only we had our adult outlook and a nice dose of hindsight as kids. Instead, as a perceptive and sensitive child, I was acutely aware that the size of my body was not acceptable by the standards of those around me. Because of that, I felt a constant awareness that there was "something wrong" with me.

I felt as though I took up too much space, and I therefore lived my life in a constant state of covert, apologetic pleasantness, never demanding or needing anything that could highlight my flaw or put me in the spotlight to be scrutinized. I learned very early on that, as a girl, my body and its size shaped my world and how I was accepted amongst the people in it.

As many kids who grow up in bigger bodies tend to experience, I was teased. I was told in no uncertain terms that my body was something to be mocked, and therefore wrong. I was a target for bullying and others' misplaced pain. My body made me feel vulnerable, as though because of it at any moment I could be hurt by someone who just wanted to be cruel.

I learned how to work around my perceived flaw, and I became very good at being good. I learned how to anticipate others' needs before they even became aware they had them. I figured out how to go along to get along. I learned how to deflate conflict around me and how to take on the feelings of others so that everyone always had a little helper when I was around. I achieved and excelled, and I did my best never to rock the boat, break the rules, or cause anyone any strife. I hid myself in the dichotomous veils of perfectionism or invisibility in hopes that no one would point out the obvious: my body was not acceptable in the culture I lived in.

This is where dieting enters the story. Once I was old enough (and sadly, that was around the age of ten) to figure out what a diet was, I erroneously came to believe there was a way out of my perceived trap. I had a way out of feeling like I was wrong, of feeling less than. In my naiveté, I believed that all I had to do was get thin, and my life would forever be "fixed." In the way it does for thousands of women in our society, the promise of thinness presented itself to me as the answer to all my problems. If only I could achieve this goal, life would be great.

My story could be the story of a million women across the globe. My dieting became my lifeline. It developed into an eating disorder by the time I was twelve, and it consumed my teenage years. It threatened my life, destroyed my self-worth, and stunted my emotional and physical development. It robbed me of my right to experience myself as a young girl becoming a young woman in a world that embraced her for what she contributed rather than what her body looked like.

But luckily for me, this is not where the story ends. This is actually where it begins. I truly believe that my experiences with dieting and disordered eating have been a gift that has pointed me to my truth. It has led me to the woman I am today and the life I now live.

I was one of the lucky ones. I woke up early from the myth that dieting was the solution to all of life's problems. I had the support and love of a wise tribe around me to help navigate my way out of the trap. I began my winding road of recovery when I was eighteen, and I became the woman I am today as a result of what I discovered through the twists and turns of the healing process. I know, without a doubt, I would not be who I am if I had not had to learn these lessons, and I see this as a blessing.

In full disclosure, this is said through the lens of hindsight. I didn't always feel this way, especially in the early days. But my own recovery and the reclamation of my self-love and respect has been the single most spiritual experience of my life. It has taught me about the true worth of a human being. It introduced me to my soul.

In fighting for my own recovery, I had no choice but to get intimate with my whole self, the shadow and the light, and embrace who I was at every moment along the journey. I had to stay with myself and learn to embrace my stumbling, my imperfection, my fear, and my pain. I had to learn how to love all the totally flawed aspects of my humanity. Without this journey of recovery, I may never have done the deep work, asked the hard questions, and had the courage to stay still long enough to hear the answers.

In changing your relationship with food and your body image, you have to commit to the change. It will require you to be deliberate and engaged in choosing to think a different way. In order to do this, you are required to unearth a long-forgotten truth: that *you are inherently worthy of something good*. And I have good news for you. Just by the nature of the fact that you are reading this book, I can tell you that you have activated that lost truth. You wouldn't have chosen to read this if you didn't, on some level, believe you deserve something better than what you have now. You have activated the core truth underneath all the lies. You *are* worthy—and it has nothing to do with what you look like or what you do or don't eat.

And this is why I see recovery as a spiritual process, one full of beauty, discovery, and awe. Recovery itself is the journey of reclaiming our inherent worthiness. It is empowerment in motion: a daily awakening of the amazing and powerful woman that you always were, and were born to be. And you thought you were just buying a book about dieting!

This book encapsulates the core of why I do what I do. Once I realized there was a better way for myself, I realized it was my passion to help empower others to realize a better way for themselves. We are so much more than the number on the scale. There is a way out the tyranny of body-image and food obsession, and teaching others how to navigate their way down this path has become my life's work.

I have discovered that there are fundamental patterns that emerge with my clients who have struggled with dieting, emotional eating, or disordered eating. While each person I see is unique, there are common, universal experiences and beliefs that emerge as obstacles. These obstacles are important for you to be aware of if you want to create a balanced relationship with food. I have identified these patterns and broken them down into ten different Diet Mindsets that create unhealthy behaviors. These Diet

Mindsets, and the behaviors they foster, harm us deeply on an emotional and psychological level. We must first learn to change these Diet Mindsets if we are to reclaim a peaceful, balanced relationship with food. They are as follows:

TEN DESTRUCTIVE DIET MINDSETS

1. The Deprivation Mindset
2. The Externalized Mindset
3. The Mean Girl Mindset
4. The Rigid Mindset
5. The ABC Mindset
6. The Take-an-Aspirin Mindset
7. The Playing Small Mindset
8. The Bureaucrat Mindset
9. The Shame-Based Mindset
10. The Misdirected-Attention Mindset

In this book, I first deconstruct the ten festructive Diet Mindsets. First you must know what you are looking for, and why it is a problem. These mindsets make up a large part of our thoughts and inner dialogue, so it is critical that you know how to recognize them.

Next, I provide you with new ways of thinking so that you can create new, healthy mindsets that support you reclaiming a balanced and respectful relationship with food. I do this with the goal of teaching you how to shift out of the insanity of traditional Diet Mindsets and strategies and into a new framework for looking at how you manage the wellness of your mind, body, and spirit.

The truth is that these ten Diet Mindsets are all part of a bigger, collective way of thinking that I see women operating from far too often. This way of thinking has become a way of being that is the cultural norm for far too many women in our society. As such, the Diet Mindsets will overlap one another and have similar properties. They weave together to form an intricate fabric representative of our collective thinking when we live our life forever obsessing about food and our bodies.

Each mindset is broken down and personified to give you an in-depth understanding of how this mindset feels, sounds, and manifests in your own life. When I asked my sister to read the manuscript of this book, she said to me, "Each mindset reminds me of its own character, kind of like an archetype . . . or better yet, kind of like that kid's movie about emotions, *Inside Out*." I loved this feedback because, while that analogy had never dawned on me, that was exactly my intention in writing the book this way.

In isolating and identifying ten different Diet Mindsets, my intention is to help you get crystal clear on the nuances and different drivers behind your thinking. I want to draw out and externalize these mindsets for each of you so that you can personally identify how your thinking is harming you, and what aspects of the Diet Mindset are sabotaging you.

Some of the ideas and action steps may feel similar, or even repetitive. That is by design! As you read the book, you will hear me talk about repetition and its role in change, but let me just set the standard up front. All learning comes through repetition. Anything that is learned is done through practice, including thought. So as you go through the exercises, be sure to remember that changing your relationship with food and changing your mindset is not that different from learning the piano in that you have to practice—and repetition is just that.

While working your way through the ten Diet Mindsets, you might find yourself wondering which of them apply to you. My experience shows me that most women who have dieted excessively or have been consumed by our diet culture relate to most of the mindsets. There may be a few that don't resonate with you, and that's fine. The goal here is not to have you take a quiz and find out where you rank with each mindset; the goal is to understand that these mindsets exist in the mind of anyone who has relied on dieting as a way of relating to her body.

Changing your mindsets is a process, not a race to the finish line. There is no timeline on the changes laid out before you in this book. These changes are a new way of relating to yourself and a paradigm shift of understanding, not a four-week program or a quick fix. Please don't rush or feel overwhelmed to have to implement everything in the book all at once. In fact, I recommend reading the book in its entirety first, then going back and beginning to implement the changes provided once you have the framework established in your mind.

Many people also find it helpful to work with a therapist, dietitian, coach, or mentor as they are making changes in their life. If you feel this would behoove you in your process, please refer to the back of the book for additional information in helping you locate the right person to help you in your journey.

It has worked for me, and I have seen it work for women and men from every walk of life. So, if you are ready to commit to leaving behind the struggle and start shifting into your best life, take a deep breath, exhale, and know you are now on the right path.

A NOTE ABOUT EATING DISORDERS AND TREATMENT

This book is not a book about eating disorders; this book is intended to help women put an end to dieting and the psychologically destructive Diet Mindsets. You will notice, however, throughout the book I often use the terms disordered eating or eating disorder. This stems from my training as an eating-disorder specialist and the fact that certain terms are just part of my language.

I also use the term disordered eating because it is my opinion that dieting and the diet culture we live in has created a widespread epidemic of disordered eating in our world. Does this mean that everyone reading this or who has ever been on a diet has an eating disorder? No.

Eating disorders are serious psychological illnesses that can only be diagnosed by a mental health professional. I cannot emphasize enough how serious they are. Eating disorders, when left untreated, have the potential to be lethal. If you have any doubt as to whether your own eating habits have led to an actual eating disorder, then I encourage you to reach out for help. There are resources at the back of this book. You can also find information about eating disorders at the NEDA (National Eating Disorder Association) website, where you can also take an online screening for eating disorders to get more information about your needs.

Even if you do not meet the criteria for an eating disorder, it is possible that your eating habits may be so out of control that you might need some assistance in dealing with them. There is nothing wrong with asking for help. In fact, in a culture that is so dysfunctional in its focus on independence, it is an act of bravery to admit that we cannot do something alone!

I encourage you to reach out to a therapist or a support group in your community if you think you might need some assistance in your journey. Knowing what your needs are and taking steps toward meeting them is an act of self-love.

Don't forget to use the resource list in the back of the book for anyone who knows they need more help or inspiration. None of us do this alone. I hope you find a tribe and wise counsel to help you navigate your path.

1

What Is a Mindset?

The greatest discovery of all time is that a person can change his future by merely changing his attitude.
—Oprah Winfrey

Before we jump into talking about the Diet Mindsets, it is important to define *mindset* itself. This word has gotten really popular in the last few years, but to understand what a mindset is and the role mindsets play in our emotional, psychological, and behavioral life, a deeper explanation is in order.

A mindset is the set of attitudes or beliefs held by a person. You can have a different mindset about different things and situations in your life. In this case, with dieting, I look at your attitude and beliefs about dieting (mindset) as the primary driver behind your actions (motivation), which is the primary influence behind how you feel (emotions) when dieting. So, your mindset influences your motivation, which in turn influences your feelings.

Throughout this book, as I teach you about the ten Diet Mindsets, I encourage you to look at your mindset as it applies to all areas of your life. As I said earlier, the Diet Mindsets are the very reason why traditional diets fail us. But they don't just fail us; they actually harm us because they allow us to integrate negative and fixed beliefs about our capabilities, our worth, and our value in this world. Remember, this book is not focused only on the mindsets involved in dieting, but what happens to our self-worth and emotional life as a result of the mindset. It is below the surface of the mindset where we discover the problem.

The destructive Diet Mindsets take hold of our belief systems and manifest in the form of low self-esteem, fear of failure, and a disheartened attitude toward making any and all changes to our relationship with food and exercise. Perhaps the most insidious fallout of relating to food with a Diet Mindset, though, is the total sense of disconnection with our bodies and our internal authority with regard to our own self-care.

For example, let's look at two different women, Andrea and Jan (these are pseudonyms, not names of actual women I've worked with).

Andrea gets up every morning at 7:00 a.m., gets to the gym, carefully prepares her meals for the day, and keeps a journal to stay aware of what she is feeling and thinking. Jan does the exact same thing.

Now let's look at mindset, or what drives their behavior.

Andrea's mindset tells her, "My body is flawed, and I'll never be acceptable until I fix the flaws of my body. I have to lose this weight. I better not eat too much, or I'm going to gain weight. I can't trust myself. I have to write down my food in my journal and track my weight, or I'm going to lose control. I've got to go the gym to work off what I have eaten. I can't gain weight. I have to lose weight to be worthy."

Jan's mindset is very different. Her mindset tells her, "I need to take care of my body; if I don't take care of myself, who will? I am tired of treating myself like crap. It's time I start to show myself some respect. Eating is a fundamental need, not something to be worried about, and being mindful of what I eat is an act of self-care. Going to the gym keeps me strong and centered, but I don't have to do it compulsively. Taking care of myself is a priority, but this is a practice, and perfection doesn't exist. I deserve to have what I want, but it's also okay to take breaks along the way."

Now, I know that these two examples are extremes, which is intentional to make my point. Very few of us actually *say* these things (at least in that language) to ourselves, but I do think variations on these beliefs can be present, silently motivating our behaviors. Do you recognize your own thoughts or beliefs in either example?

In the examples, one is extremely damaging and the other is extremely empowering. The behaviors may look similar (intentional choices with food, journaling, and exercise), but the long-term psychological and emotional implications for each example are vastly different.

In the first example with Andrea, which is an example of a Diet Mindset, the changes in behavior will end up being self-destructive. In the second example with Jan, the changes in behavior will be sustainable and self-developing. The reasons for this are explained in the following chapters, where we will look deeper into the psychology and nuances of the ten destructive Diet Mindsets.

2

The Diet Mindset

We do not need magic to change the world, we carry all the power we need inside ourselves already: we have the power to imagine better.

—J. K. Rowling

Now that we understand that a Diet Mindset does not work, let's explore the issue further. Before we dig in, however, I want to take an in-depth look at how the following chapters will explore the Diet Mindsets and give you the information you need in order to change.

In the following chapters, each mindset will be broken down into four parts:

1. The Mindset Name
2. The Mindset Type
3. (What the) Mindset Sounds Like
4. The Mindset Cause

I did this intentionally to give you different options for how you remember and relate to the mindset as you explore your own thinking and behavior. Not everyone learns and retains information in the same way, so with each Diet

Mindset, you have options for how you want to identify and classify them.

Mindset Name is a catchy identifier that captures the essence of the mindset and creates an easy-to-remember mental association with the mindset, one that your brain will recall with ease. Think of it like a memorable brand or visual logo that is going to make each mindset easy to recall. You can't change what you aren't aware of, so I want to help you identify these mindsets as quickly and with as much ease as is possible!

Mindset Type is a deeper dive into the type of thinking that creates that particular Diet Mindset. By naming the type, I categorize each Diet Mindset in a way that allows you to see its overall substance. When we become familiar with the different types of thinking, we can start to see patterns within our own thoughts and behaviors that might fall into these different categories.

Mindset Sounds Like: If this mindset were reduced to a simple statement, something you told yourself over and over again, this is what the particular mindset would sound like. Because our mindset is part of an internalized belief system, it manifests not only as behavior but also as thought. Our inner thoughts are nothing more than the conversations we have with ourselves about our life as it is passing us by. By learning to listen to the content of these inner conversations, we can more easily identify different Diet Mindsets.

Mindset Cause will identify what is behind the thinking, otherwise known as the etiology. The cause gives you a label for what causes each particular Diet Mindset in the first place. Each section will go into detail regarding the cause and will explain the cause-and-effect pattern in an effort to help you identify if any of these issues are plaguing your own relationship with food. If we don't get to the cause, we struggle to change the underlying pattern, so understanding the mindset cause plays a vital role in the change process itself.

Each chapter will also conclude with what I feel is such an important piece of any self-help, psychology, or personal development book, which is HOW TO CHANGE!

I've read more of these types of books than I care to admit, and I find that, all too often, the books are very good at identifying the problem but don't spend nearly enough time discussing the solution. This book comes with solutions!

Each chapter will include an **Action Steps** section, which will give you new mindset shifts (new ways of thinking) and behavior modifications (that's the dry and clinical way of saying things you can *actually do* to make changes). I recommend that you procure a journal or specific document on your computer to use as you read this book, as some of the activities ask that you take time to write (or at the very least deeply ponder) your thoughts and feelings.

Each chapter will also include a **Summary** section. I have included this because the brain loves repetition. It also likes small, short summaries so it can remember larger concepts in a concise and easy way. In these sections, I have highlighted the major points from each chapter, so you can go back at any time and review the takeaway for each Diet Mindset as you are learning and changing your thinking.

One last thing: Not by design, but nevertheless, my past and present work has subsisted of mostly working with women. It is important that I state outright that it is not only women who struggle with unhealthy relationships with food and body image. I do, however, own the tendency to use the feminine pronoun, and as such, I want to speak to any men who may be reading this book. Many men who have dieted and struggled with food will identify and understand the concepts in this book. There really is not one thing in this book that cannot be applied to you and your journey. Just change the pronoun, and own it as yours. My intention is never to exclude anyone.

So . . . are you ready to begin to change your relationship with food? Are you ready to begin a new way of thinking, and thus a new way of living? Are you ready to reclaim what was once yours and is your inherent right—a peaceful and balanced relationship with food and with your body?

Can I get a yes? Can I get a hell yes? (Okay, I'll take a heck yes, but put some muscle behind it.)

Then let's go!

3

The Deprivation Mindset

Abundance is not something we acquire. It is something we tune into.

—Wayne Dyer

Diet Mindset #1: The Deprivation Mindset
Type: A Lack Mindset
Sounds Like: "There are only certain foods you can eat; the rest are off limits."
Cause: Deprivation Syndrome

How classic is the tale of the person who starts a diet on Monday (because let's face it, who starts a diet on a Tuesday?) and does really "good" until about Thursday afternoon, when the stress of the week takes its toll? By Friday evening, it's an all-out binge fest as the once successful dieter has lost control and can't seem to stop eating. This, folks, is what happens when we activate what is known as **deprivation syndrome**.

Do you remember science class and Newton's third law of motion? (In full self-disclosure, I had to google it to be sure, so it's okay if you don't.) It states that every action has an equal and opposite reaction. I bet Newton wasn't thinking of dieting when he was developing his genius, but his law applies to most things, and dieting is certainly one of them.

If you go on a diet that feels in any way restrictive, your automatic reaction is going to be *equal* to in intensity, but in the *opposite* direction of that feeling of restriction. In other words, the more deprived you feel, the more the urge to eat will grow.

Action (restrictive dieting) = Reaction (food cravings/binge eating)

Perhaps the most powerful illustration of the effects of restrictive dieting and weight loss on behavior is an experimental study conducted more than fifty years ago and published in 1950 by Ancel Keys and his colleagues at the University of Minnesota.

Let's take a minute and look further into this study. It might get a little dry and clinical, but bear with me and get through this part. It sets the stage for *why* our brains get fixated in the mindsets we are trying to change. If you have ever said, "I know better—why can't I do better?" this section will explain that and help you see it has nothing to do with your strength and character. Plus, it's brief and pretty fascinating to see how actual research explains what has been happening to you all along!

The experiment involved studying thirty-six young, healthy men while restricting their calorie intake. During the first phase of the experiment, the men ate normally while their eating patterns were recorded. This established a baseline for "normal eating."

During the next period, the men were restricted to approximately half of their former food intake and lost, on average, approximately 25 percent of their former weight. It is important to note that cutting the men's food intake in half (to an average of 1,570 calories) is not unlike that of many diets in our culture today. Sadly, I know many diets that require far fewer calories. Six months of weight loss were followed by three months during which the men were slowly allowed to increase their calorie intake.

Although the levels of overall weight loss varied considerably, the men experienced dramatic physical, psychological, and social changes. In most cases, these changes remained long after the experiment was over. One of the greatest changes that occurred in the men was a dramatic increase in food obsession. The men found concentration on their usual activities increasingly difficult because they became plagued by incessant thoughts of food and eating (sound familiar?). During the refeeding phase of the experiment, many of the men felt their appetites had increased. The men felt out of control with their cravings for food, and found that they were eating constantly.

Even after the three months of eating normally, the men reported increased hunger immediately following a large meal. After about five months of refeeding, the majority of the men reported some normalization of their eating patterns, but for some, the tendency toward overeating and food preoccupation continued (Garner, D. M. 1998).

So why does this happen? In order to better understand this, we need to take a look at our ancestors and look at how our brains have developed over time.

Beneath our highly evolved intellect, humans have the same basic, primal survival needs that all animals on the planet have. We have to eat, drink, and breathe to stay alive and evolve our species. Deprivation syndrome can be understood only by understanding our basic need for survival.

Abraham Maslow, a psychologist and all-around really smart guy, established long ago that, in a hierarchy of needs, the primary survival needs will always trump needs that are considered less necessary for survival. In other words, if it comes down to choosing between eating and improving one's self-esteem, eating will win every time.

When you diet, the parts of your brain that are wired to be on the lookout for deprivation, the brain stem and the limbic system, get triggered (Siegel 2012). People commonly refer to this part of the brain as the **reptilian brain** or the **lizard brain**. Our lizard brain is the oldest, least-evolved part of the brain and is the seat of our most primitive instincts and urges, such as our basic drive to survive. You've heard of the flight/fight/freeze response to a threat, right? Our lizard brain controls that response, along with our drive to feed ourselves (Harris 2016).

Our intellectual capacity, which is also the ability to use reason and logic, is housed in the frontal lobe of our brain, in an area known as the prefrontal cortex. The frontal-lobe region of the brain has evolved as humans have evolved as a species, and it is capable of processing more today than when our ancestors were out roaming the wilderness, hunting and gathering for food. The same cannot be said about our reptilian brain. It is still running on the assumption that we are out hunting and gathering our food in the desert somewhere.

When you diet or deprive yourself of food in any way, the reptilian brain receives the message that there is a shortage of food. This message then activates your survival response, which triggers you to seek out food. The brain does this by increasing your mental focus on food and your cravings for food, otherwise known as that insatiable desire to eat anything and everything that you start to feel around day three of your diet. This is why the Deprivation Mindset is a lack mindset—because the mindset is only focused on what is not there, what is lacking. Your brain does this out of fear and out of its primitive need to survive.

So imagine, here you are, in the present day, and you are trying to change your relationship with food. But when you do so in a way that makes you feel deprived, your old pal the reptilian brain reads your restriction of food as deprivation, or as a threat. It has no idea that we are way beyond the days of hunting and gathering. It doesn't know that we have endured agricultural and industrial revolutions and now exist in a world of convenience and grocery stores and at-home pizza delivery. All it knows is that deprivation means threat. It thinks that there must be some kind of famine or drought, and its only goal is to help you hoard as much food as you can to survive the impending shortage that the feeling of deprivation signals.

Like a squirrel foraging and hoarding away nuts for the winter, you find yourself thinking about food all the time. It's as if the craving for what you can't have takes over your every thought. You can fight it with white knuckles, but eventually the will to stick to your diet is going to be overridden by the reptilian brain's desire to keep you alive. Again, it has no idea that you are actually safe and that you *want* this deprivation. All it knows is that deprivation equals shortage of food equals threat to survival.

The Deprivation Mindset isn't something that can be ignored or that you can use "willpower" to push through. It is part of your psychological drive to survive, and survival always wins out in the battle of needs. A mindset filled with thoughts about what you can't have, shouldn't eat, aren't able to do, etc. leads to a series of brain activity that makes it really very difficult to follow your desired behavior. Focus on what isn't there, and the mind will see to it that it works equally as hard to find what it can to replace the perceived lack.

This leads to yo-yo dieting, which is so common it's practically a cultural norm. Back and forth we go from effort to failure, gaining more weight every time we do. Every time you start a new diet after you have come out of a non-diet, perhaps binge-filled period, you are reinforcing the idea of shortage and threat to your reptilian brain. It reinforces the idea that it is never safe and that it is important to always be seeking and hoarding food.

No one likes to yo-yo. It's frustrating and defeating and makes you feel as though nothing you do will work. The key is to stop the back and forth—to stop the swinging.

The imagery I use a lot in sessions with my clients is that of being on a swing set, swinging back and forth. Try to picture it. Remember being on the swings when you were younger, pumping your legs to get higher so that the swing would thrust you forward and up with equal force? The higher up you pumped, the faster and higher you would swing. That's the image I want you to remember here. That is the visual for the force behind the deprivation/craving/binge cycle.

An extremely restrictive diet is like pulling that swing back as high as it will go. As soon as you let go (also known as stopping your diet, and we all know that is bound to happen at some point), that swing is going to swing all the way to the other end.

I'll be the first to admit, I loved swinging. I bet I still would if I ever got to a playground. But there is something to be said about getting off and having my feet on solid ground. Staying on the swing and never getting off would make me sick, which is a good metaphor for what happens when our life is a constant swinging from one extreme to the other—from all to nothing.

All-or-nothing (or dichotomous) behavior, which is another way of describing this swing between dieting and indulging, is inherent in most diet programs and virtually all Diet Mindsets. This dichotomous thinking and behavior hurts us in the long run. Like swinging, at first it can be fun—exciting, even. However, we can't sustain it, and our efforts end up falling apart and making us sick.

The bottom line here is that any time you do something that makes you feel deprived, you automatically kick in your "equal-action response."

- You feel deprived and want to rebel.
- You are starving, so all you can think about is food.
- The more you restrict, the more you want to eat.

The good news about understanding the Deprivation Mindset is that we can prevent it by choosing to reframe our eating in ways that do not activate the high swing in the first place. I have helped countless people learn to reframe their mindsets to avoid the "swing" and maintain stability in their behavior, and you can do it too!

ACTION STEPS

1. Focus on What You Love—Create a Love List

The solution is always inherently exposed in the problem itself. The Deprivation Mindset is a lack mindset. In order to break this mindset, we must move our thoughts into abundance. It is critical that in order to change the Deprivation Mindset, you begin focusing on breaking down the rules that you currently have around food that have come from years of dieting.

Traditional dieting is all about what you should not eat. It is predicated around focusing on eliminating foods from your diet (thus triggering your reptilian brain to seek out food—what a trap!). We are going to change that going forward. The new mindset must be about focusing on all the things you can eat. Sounds kind of scary, right? Trusting yourself to eat food is a whole new paradigm, but you have to start somewhere.

I know it can be a daunting thought, but in order to bust apart the Deprivation Mindset, you must convince your brain that food is plentiful. There must be a prolonged period (we are not just talking a week or two here) where the brain repeatedly experiences one critical thing: you feeding yourself and feeling a positive emotion about your food choices. This will signal to your brain that, indeed, the harvest has come in this year and that the rains are coming down. In other words, there is no drought, there is no famine, and there is an abundance of food, so it can calm down and stop foraging.

Here is how I suggest you begin doing that. I want you to create a love list of foods. We must begin to tell the brain that there are foods that we love to eat (thus sending the basic message that food is abundant).

Which foods go on our love list? Foods that feel nurturing and nourishing to our bodies. Foods that feel rewarding while also feeling good in our bodies. I am going to shy away from calling this food healthy, as the word healthy has unfortunately become synonymous with the negative Diet Mindsets and, in many ways, is just code for acceptable by diet standards. Watch this subtle but important semantic here; the brain will interpret a healthy list as an old Diet Mindset and trigger the feeling of deprivation. Referring to food itself as healthy can be triggering for some, so I do suggest you check in with yourself around that. I, however, think it's important that we reclaim the words healthy and health. That is why I chose to use that word in the subtitle of this book. True health is about looking at ourselves in a comprehensive, holistic way, incorporating our minds and souls along with our bodies. As women, we deserve to realize that our health and the health of our bodies has to do with so much more than eating a certain way or managing our weight. Being balanced, living without shame, and choosing to make decisions about your body from your own inner wisdom is what I think being healthy is, and that is why this book's subtitle intentionally uses that word. It's time we redefine it, so hopefully the young women who are babies right now can grow up understanding what balanced, empowered health looks like.

I want you to identify five foods that feel like love food for you. They are foods you would buy your best friend or child if they were home sick and needed to be nurtured. They are foods you would make sure your child ate on a regular basis if you were responsible for feeding them. They are probably full of nutrients because we often care more about other people's health than we do our own. But some people might have sweets or treats on their list, and that's okay too. This exercise is about giving yourself permission to eat and beginning to undo the old dichotomous "good/bad" food list, so try to just trust what feels right and not to question your food choice too much. If you are encouraging eating, it is working.

As you change your relationship with food over time, add to this list when you identify foods that you feel really great about eating. It's important that these foods satisfy you as much as they nourish you. Don't throw lettuce on there just because your old mindset tells you to. Let's call a spade a spade—I've never met anyone who liked lettuce without the dressing, so don't cheat yourself here. Satiety, or how satisfied we feel mentally after eating, is an important part of the equation when considering fullness. One could theoretically eat enough lettuce to fill their stomach, but they would never feel satisfied.

The bottom line is that in order to deactivate the Deprivation Mindset, we must stop focusing on the absence of food or what foods we can't eat, and begin focusing on the presence of food, namely all the foods we love to eat. We have to shift from fearing food to loving it.

2. Add Food Instead of Eliminating Food

This action step expands on Action Step #1 (create a love list of foods). If you are just starting out, I would encourage you to begin to just focus on adding your love foods into your diet more and more. Once you have done this and feel they are routinely part of your staple weekly intake, then add something else. Maybe you know you need more energy and therefore need more carbohydrates in your diet. Pick one or two sources of carbohydrates and focus on adding them into your meals. Maybe you know you want more variety in your diet, so focus on the rainbow of foods you can create. Perhaps you know you want a more balanced diet, so focus on what food groups are missing and focus on choosing foods that represent the missing nutrients and create more balance. In order to override the Deprivation Mindset, you must reverse your thinking. Focus on adding food instead of eliminating food to aid in that reversal.

For any of you so indoctrinated by Diet Mindsets that you read this and think, *If I add more food, I'll just gain weight, and that is unhealthy*, it's important to note here how your thinking is erred, and I encourage you to pause and reflect. Health comes from balance, and from listening to our bodies and responding with efficiency and kindness. This reduces stress by allowing you to flow with the true nature of your being (flexible, not rigid) and provides a feeling of safety and security because you are getting your needs met. For every turn of the page you make in this book, the old Diet Mindset, which comes from our destructive diet culture, will challenge you with scare tactics and old beliefs. Do not be so easily duped. Try to keep an open mind and decide for yourself when you are done with the book.

Upon hearing these action steps, many of my clients are terrified that this new thinking will lead to out-of-control behavior with food. They are convinced that if they give themselves permission to eat and make food abundant, they might start eating and never stop. If you fear this same thing, I hear you and I empathize, as your fear is valid. But please trust that it is coming from the part of your brain that is deprived from years of dieting or restrictive eating. People without this history of deprivation do not share in this fear, which should illustrate that this urge is an effect, not a cause.

You fear that the desire to eat anything and everything in sight *equals* nonstop binging. The truth is you've left out a piece of that equation. You haven't factored in the role that dieting and deprivation play. Dieting and deprivation *equals* the desire to eat everything in sight and leads to nonstop binging.

So rest assured that if you remove the original cause, the whole equation eventually loses its cause-and-effect relationship. Much like my metaphor of the swing, by adding foods you love and allowing yourself permission to eat, you are refusing to pull back on the swing and pump your legs, thus reducing the force of the momentum and eventually stopping the swing.

You may find that initially you do want to indulge in the things you have made forbidden for years. This is normal. Every swing that stopped swinging had to rock back and forth a few times before it came to a complete stop. But if you commit to refusing to go back on a diet or restricting your food and creating that feeling of deprivation in the first place, you will find your way back to balance sooner than you think.

The body is always seeking balance. Always. In medicine, they refer to this as homeostasis. This applies to appetite, and this is partially why the yo-yo cycle exists. Knowing this, we are reversing the motion and reclaiming the balance we once had with food before all this diet nonsense got us out of whack.

SUMMARY

1. Focusing on what we can't have signals the brain to obsess over that very thing. This is called **deprivation syndrome**.
2. Breaking the Deprivation Mindset requires that we focus on what we can eat and release the restriction around what foods are off limits.

3. Create a **love list** that includes foods you *can* eat that are both satisfying and that feel like good choices for nourishing your body.
4. One by one, increase the amount of love foods in your diet instead of eliminating foods, so that the brain has time to trust that there is no longer a shortage of food.

4

The Externalized Mindset

When we give up dieting, we take back something we were often too young to know we had given away: our own voice. Our ability to make decisions about what to eat and when. Our belief in ourselves. Our right to decide what goes into our mouths. Unlike the diets that appear monthly in magazines or the thermal pants that sweat off pounds, unlike a lover or a friend or a car, your body is reliable. It doesn't go away, get lost, stolen. If you will listen, it will speak.

—Geneen Roth, *Breaking Free from Emotional Eating*

Diet Mindset #2: The Externalized Mindset
Type: A Helpless Mindset
Sounds Like: "I can't trust myself with food; I need an expert to tell me what to eat."
Cause: Reliance on External Knowledge versus Internal Wisdom

When you pick up any diet book or read about the newest fad diet on the internet, inevitably it tells you what to eat, and sometimes when to eat, right? The odd thing about that is—how does *it* know? Really, ask yourself the question. How does the book (or the person writing the book) know what we need to eat? How does it know if we are hungry? How does it know what we like, our palate, and our preferences?

Well, the truth is, it doesn't. But here is the clincher in all of this: the problem is that, chances are, neither do you because you've been dieting for so long.

Diets pretend to know what we need and what is best for us. Some expert in nutrition tells us to eat this or eat that and promises us that it is going to be "the answer" to our problems. We believe, we follow, we try, and most often, we struggle. This struggle leads to what we perceive as failure and then total frustration. The person with the answers either led us down the wrong path, or there is just something inherently wrong with us because we couldn't make the promised solution amount to anything.

This leads us to Diet Mindset #2, the Externalized Mindset. This mindset is a helpless mindset predicated around the reliance on external authority versus using your internal wisdom.

You are the expert on *you*. Only you know what you want to eat, when you are hungry, and what your body is craving. You were born with the ability to know when to eat and how much to eat. This knowledge is what I refer to as your **internal wisdom**.

When a baby is hungry, it will get fussy and start crying. They just *know*. And when they are full, they will stop eating and refuse to take the bottle or nipple. They don't binge. They just stop. And that knowing is still inside of you—

except many of us have detached ourselves from that knowing by giving away our power to external forces.

We come by this mindset honestly. As people, I think we are trained to seek our truth outside of ourselves. Think about it. We are born utterly dependent, so in order to survive, we must look to our caretakers to do everything for us. We literally depend on them for everything for the first decade or two of our lives (the extent of that dependence declines as we grow).

Then, at some point, we wake up . . . and we are "adults" (I use quotes because there is not a sarcasm font). Chronologically, this is said to happen when we hit eighteen, but for most people, it is much later than that. Either way, whenever we hit adulthood, we are catapulted into a new paradigm—one in which all of a sudden we are supposed to be the expert. We are in charge, yet we come to this place with very little on-the-job training.

This dependence on others as the source of "the truth" extends way beyond childhood. It is how we are programmed to see the world. We see it in workplaces, where most people look to a boss or a company to lead the way and provide for them. Government and organized groups (political, religious, etc.) also mirror our early childhood (or family-of-origin) experience. Everywhere we go we are looking outside of ourselves for the rules, for the answers, and for validation that we are doing the right thing.

I know this not because I sit on some haughty, high intellectual perch, where I am impervious to this feeling, but because I am every bit as trained to be human as every one of you reading this. I know all too well what it's like to feel as though power and authority are something I have to seek externally.

This belief, however, leads to giving away your power and falling prey to feeling like a victim. We can become victims of society and the unhealthy standards currently being fed to us. We can become victims of the manipulation of a commercial industry whose main marketing strategy is to perpetuate the belief that we are not enough as we are, so we will continue to buy "stuff" to feel better about ourselves. In her book, *The Beauty Myth*, Naomi Wolf states this with eloquence: "A culture fixated on female thinness is not an obsession about female beauty, but an obsession about female obedience" (Wolfe 1990, 187).

It is our job to become critical thinkers and decide for ourselves what really matters. We have to become very clear on our own morals, values, and beliefs, then ask ourselves if the way we relate to our bodies and to food reflects our deeper belief about what it means to be here on this earth. This extends far beyond looking to a diet to tell us what to eat. It is about learning to trust your own authority and seeking your own counsel first before you look to others for validation or answers.

Let's look at body image. First, take a few minutes to reflect on what you really value. What are your deepest, most beloved things in this world? What really matters to you? Now, compare these core values with your beliefs about your body. Do they seem congruent?

Do you believe in compassion and tolerance, yet have a deeply critical relationship with yourself when it comes to eating and your body?

Do you believe that the worth of a human being is about more than how they look, yet you place all your own value in the numbers on a scale every morning?

Once we start taking a closer look, we see that our relationship with our body is often deeply in conflict with our inner values. We have sought our answers outside of ourselves, only to embrace beliefs that don't align with who we really are.

The same is probably true of how you relate to food. Other "experts"—the diets, the well-meaning authors and specialists, etc.—have replaced our internal understanding of our own hunger and how to feed ourselves with *their* beliefs, and *their* truth, and *their* philosophy on change. We have come to believe that there is some other force that has the answer for us, when in reality, the answers are discovered inside of us.

Psychotherapist Sheldon Kopp has a book with a humorous title that alludes to this principle. The book is called *If You Meet the Buddha on the Road, Kill Him!* The title refers to the dangers in thinking that someone else knows what is best for you. They don't. There are no gurus out there with the answer (and if you meet someone who wants you to believe otherwise, it's a danger you want to avoid). The answer isn't in my book either, which is the point I am hoping to convey. The answer lies within you.

I clearly remember working with a specific client around this issue. She told me she is afraid of being alone, or worse, being bored. I asked her why boredom was something she feared, and she paused, then answered, "I don't know. I just don't know what to do with myself. I feel nervous and restless."

We went on to explore what she might WANT to do with the time she had, the literal time (hours, minutes) that she otherwise felt restless and bored. She paused and reflected, and eventually she came close to tears.

"I don't know" was her reply. "I have no idea what I want to do—no idea what I want."

She is not alone. This is a common response I hear from clients, in many different forms. They do not really know what they want, and they are also afraid to turn toward themselves to seek out the answer. Because they have spent most of their lives looking to the outside for validation and guidance, they do not have an established relationship with themselves, and frankly, they do not feel they know themselves at all.

"I don't know who I am" is a response I hear a lot on the couch. And it is almost always followed up with the acknowledgment of fear and anxiety around the idea of discovering who they are. If you don't know who you are, then is it any wonder that it is hard to know what you want to eat, and difficult to trust yourself with making decisions around food, or anything for that matter?

- What do you love to do for fun?
- What are your passions?
- What things in life are you drawn to?
- What relaxes you?
- What do you yearn for?

For many people, these questions are difficult to answer. I believe that in our culture we are being distracted and misled to an epidemic degree. Our cultural obsession with thinness, dieting, and our bodies has countless numbers of young men and women hypnotized into believing that the point of their existence is to be ornamental.

So many people I meet are constantly focused on things that are external, be it their aesthetic body, their latest diet, their weight, taking care of others, or trying to please the world at large. As a result, they never have the opportunity to look inward, connect with their own truth, and recognize their own powerful potential.

Chronic dieting and food restriction divide us from our true, authentic self. They hold our attention on the outside, causing us to miss vital bonding and attachment time with *our self*, with who we really are, our essential self, our soul.

By the time most of us hit adulthood, if we have been food and body-image obsessed, or on chronic diets since our early teens, we arrive at the pivotal stage of adulthood full of negative beliefs about our body and our worth. We also have little to no knowledge of who we truly are.

We are empty and hungry, on the inside and out. Sadly, the only answer we have as to how to "fix it" is to go on another diet.

If you could go back in time and reclaim all the hours that you have spent dieting, worrying about your weight, obsessing about food (what you will eat, can't eat, won't get to eat, or eat too much of), or being unhappy with some aspect of your body . . . how much time do you think you would get back?

How much time would you have if you could reclaim all the time spent trying to be pleasing or perfect?

What span of time would you have if you collected all the time trying to take care of others' needs, run their lives, and be perfect at all of it?

Now, imagine that you could spend that time doing something you felt deeply connected to. Imagine being immersed in something that you feel passionate about, or something that brings you a deep sense of joy.

For those of you out there saying, "Um . . . I don't have a clue what that would be," for the sake of argument, let's just say you could use that time having fun. Whatever you chose, imagine that time is yours to *feel* happy and be utterly content with life.

How do you think this would impact your life? If not your life, then how could this change impact the lives of others?

ACTION STEPS

1. Seek Your Own Counsel

Pay attention to yourself the way you would pay attention to a new friend, someone whom you genuinely like and are interested in.

Pay attention to your internal reactions.

- What draws your attention?
- What makes you smile?
- What makes your body respond when you see it or experience it?

When we work on this issue, the first thing I tell clients is "From now on, when someone talks about something or asks you a question, I want your first inner response to be 'What do I think and feel about this?'"

This seems painfully obvious to some, but for those who have lived a life trying to please the outside world, it is not usually the go-to question. Our usual first response is something closer to "What *should* I do or think?" or "What is the *correct* response here?" or "What do *they* need or want from me in this situation?" It is about someone else's needs or wants, and it isn't seeking the answer from within based on our own values or what makes us feel good.

I am not suggesting we don't consider others' opinions here, but rather that our opinion is the first we seek, before we look to others to guide us or give us a benchmark for what is pleasing. We must be the ultimate counsel, the majority stakeholder with the most shares whose vote has the most weight and who has ultimate vetoing authority over the rest.

Need something a little bit more tangible to work with? Then start with something we are all familiar with. Start with food.

Like with most things, our relationship with food will often parallel our relationships with ourselves and others. If you don't know who you are and what you like and dislike, it could be a deductive conclusion that you are also disconnected with food.

Let's assume your life with food is guided by external rules. *Low calorie, high calorie, organic, healthy, high fat, gluten this or that, blah, blah . . .*

I cannot emphasize this enough: forget the rules! For every rule, there is a contradictory rule that also demands that it is true. These rules are just someone else's truth.

Obviously, if you have a health condition or diagnosed illness that prevents you from eating a certain thing, then you should honor your body and not eat foods that make you ill. I do find that some people, however, will attach to presumed food allergies or conditions without a formal diagnosis as a way of avoiding, restricting, or dieting. This is a reckoning moment within yourself that only you can truly answer.

Dig deep and be honest with yourself around what rules you have created and why. If you genuinely know that eating certain foods makes you feel sick, then it is wise to avoid these foods. But if you hear your wise voice inside telling you that what is really motivating you is something more in line with an old Diet Mindset, then justifying your decisions is only going to lead you back toward self-sabotage and toward the psychological stress that always comes as a result of approaching food through a Diet Mindset.

Dietary science, guidelines, and information are not bad. In fact, it's necessary that we know what we are putting in our bodies in order to understand how to best fuel our bodies and care for our health. Once you get to know yourself and your patterns with food, you can always refer back to the science and guidelines to help guide you (not control you). There is a huge difference between a guideline and a rule. The difference is that the guideline is there to guide the person in charge—which is you—whereas with a rule, it is the rule itself that dictates the situation. Like a law, the rule is in charge of your behavior whether you like it or not. See the difference?

Ask yourself, what would taste good? What would feel good in your body? What would fuel you? What do *you want*?

You will probably get a variety of responses that run the gamut from brownies to broccoli, and that's okay. You are deep. You have many layers. Metaphorically speaking, you are both brownies and broccoli (and that's what makes you so interesting!).

Don't be afraid of what you find. Take it one step at a time. You will be okay. This leads us to the second opportunity for change, which is to practice mindful eating.

2. *Practice Mindful Eating*

The practice of mindful eating and breaking the dieting lifestyle can lead the way back to yourself and open the doorway to getting to know your other "likes" and "dislikes." The more you refer back to yourself and seek the answer within, the more you build a deep connection with yourself.

Mindful eating, and what I describe as working with your **authentic appetite**, are all phrases that express the same basic notion. Here is how I explain it, broken down to its most basic components:

- We are all born intuitively knowing when we are hungry, when we are full, and what we do and don't enjoy eating. We come here with the tools to feed ourselves. We are born with a perfectly healthy relationship with food.
- Years of being told what to eat and how to eat combined with dieting and various other wacky ways of relating to food destroy this innate knowledge over time.
- We have the ability to come back to our inner knowing through mindfulness—that is, paying attention to ourselves when we eat. Slowing down. Being aware. Paying attention to our body's subtle (and not-so-subtle) signals. Asking questions of ourselves before, during, and after we eat.
- Mindful eating allows us to reconnect to our wants and needs regarding food. It is also a way of reconnecting with our deeper needs, our soul self, which is a fundamentally necessary connection to sustain any change. It's about trusting ourselves again. It's about recognizing that we are the authority over what we need, want, and desire—be it food or anything in our lives (as you are learning, it is rarely just about food).

How do you actually practice mindful eating?

- Listen to your hunger cues and get to know what hunger and fullness feel like.
- Feed yourself when you are hungry, and stop when you are full.
- Ask these questions when you are choosing what you might want to eat:
  - What does my body need to be nourished (nutrition)?
  - What am I craving?
  - Will I enjoy eating it?
  - How will my body feel after I eat it?

These questions help align you with three basic components of connecting with your authentic appetite—nutrients, satiety, and portion equivalent to hunger. We need to be mindful of all three in order to feel truly satiated.

It is possible to consistently eat beyond fullness and still be malnourished. If you are not getting the right nutrients in your diet, you can eat all food all day and your body will still send out hunger cues in hopes that you will feed it the nutrients it needs. This is because your need for nutrients has not been met.

If you constantly eat foods you do not like and that do not satisfy (satiation) you, then you can fill your stomach beyond fullness and you will still crave food. This is because your need for satiety has not been met.

If you only eat portions that are predetermined before you get hungry for that particular meal, then you are not honoring your need for portion relative to hunger. Each day we have differing amounts of activity and energy output, so each time we get hungry, we are hungry for a different amount of food. We cannot meet this need if we are following a prepackaged, predetermined portion control. This is because your need for portion equivalent to hunger has not been met.

You have to feed your body nutritionally while making sure you don't feel deprived, while at the same time making sure you eat enough to satisfy your hunger in that moment based on what your body needs in the present. In order to do all of this, we must be mindfully aware of what is happening in the moment with food and our bodies as we eat.

Your body tells you what it needs. If you start listening, you can learn to read your inner signals and connect with the internal knowing that guides you as you make food choices. Many of us are completely disconnected from this wisdom, so give yourself time to reconnect and understand that this is a process.

3. *Pause before You Act/Eat*

Being mindful with food often requires us to sit with food cravings and choose not to act on them until we check in with ourselves to figure out what is really going on. We feel the strong urges, and yet rather than act, we observe the desire and we are curious about its origin. We ask questions of ourselves, such as:

- Am I really hungry?
- Is this emotional or physical hunger?
- If it is physical hunger, what does my body want, and what does it need?
- If it isn't physical, what am I really hungry for?

Paying attention to ourselves when we are eating is a practice, so please use that word literally. The good news is most of us have at least three chances (three meals) to do that every single day. Mindful eating is a practice that must be learned. You must know that you are developing (or rediscovering, to be more accurate) a skill set, but like all things worth having, it takes time. So, pausing and slowing down is a skill you must start practicing today. This is about progress, not perfection.

Learning to trust ourselves takes time. If you met someone on the street, would you trust them inherently? I hope not. It is necessary to have doubts and boundaries in order to keep yourself safe. Trust is not something that occurs quickly, and there is no quick way to override that, any more than you can override the body's response to feeling deprived (we must learn our survival responses and work with, not against them!). Trust is earned, and it is developed through trustworthy behaviors and repetition.

As we start to pay attention to our hunger, we start to make a new connection with ourselves. As you listen to your needs and wants, you start to feel seen by the person who is most critical to your self-worth—you! This process is as much about learning how to trust yourself as it is about learning how to reconnect with your hunger cues. This process is about redefining your relationship with yourself.

SUMMARY

1. We are primed to seek our wisdom from those outside of ourselves.
2. In doing this, we become disconnected from our inner wisdom, both with regard to how we live our lives and with the food choices we make.
3. In order to reverse this trend, we must:

i. Seek our own counsel first and foremost, always making sure our inner wisdom and needs trump that of the external world.
ii. Practice **mindful eating**, which asks that we stay present and aware while eating food, applying curiosity and attention to our behaviors and motivations.
iii. Pause before we act, and sit with our cravings before we indulge them in order to understand the valuable communication held within the urge. Urges are our bodies' way of communicating with us, and we must be mindful and present to hear it.

5

The Mean Girl Mindset

Calling someone else fat won't make you any skinnier. Calling someone else stupid won't make you any smarter.

—Cady Heron (Lindsay Lohan's character) in *Mean Girls*

Diet Mindset #3: The Mean Girl Mindset
Type: Critical Mindset
Sounds Like: "You can't eat that. What's wrong with you? You need to lose weight."
Cause: The Jerk Boss Syndrome

Most everyone knows the cultural reference to the "mean girl." There was even a movie about it. *Mean Girls* portrays a story about that group of girls in high school who were cutthroat, snarky, image obsessed, and cruel. They were the pack of popular girls who roamed the halls, demeaning those whom they deemed less than, and making their lives a living hell.

I imagine that after that description, your reaction to the question "Are you a mean girl?" is "NO! Of course not!"

But I invite you to think deeply about this one.

- Are you snarky toward and critical of yourself?
- Do you never allow yourself to accept genuine compliments?
- Do you compare yourself with other women and their bodies?
- Do you critically police your food intake and get mean if you don't comply with your diet?
- Do you force yourself to go hungry?
- Do you say snarky and nasty things about your body when you see pictures or look in the mirror?
- Do you feel threatened by women you feel are beautiful?

If you are answering yes to some of these questions, then you are identifying your own personal "mean girl." She lives in your mind, following you around everywhere you go, criticizing, judging, and essentially making fun of you.

And maybe, just maybe, she influences the way you feel about other women as well. This is a hard one to come to terms with. Nobody wants to see themselves in a negative light, but for the sake of healing, I encourage you to keep an open mind.

It is not uncommon for women to compete with one another. It is also widely recognized that women do gossip about other women and criticize one another for perceived shortcomings. Why do we do this? Are we just superficial and catty (and all the other awful stereotypes about women that exist in the collective realm)?

I say no; I believe it is quite the contrary.

When we are catty, we are actually afraid. When we judge another, we ourselves are insecure. We are taught that we aren't good enough, so we are reach outside of ourselves to make sure that we aren't alone in our perceived inadequacy.

We strive to feel powerful, and by knocking someone else down, we might temporarily feel bigger, better, or somehow superior to the person in question. The sad irony in this scenario is that our power is diminished every time we judge and compare. Every time we engage in this way, we are confirming our own insecurities. We are essentially turning to our inner mean girl and saying, "Everything you tell me about how unworthy I am is right."

If we allow our inner mean girl to run the show, then competition and comparison will always muddy our relationships with others. When we ourselves feel empowered, we are no longer afraid of empowering one another. I don't have to knock you down to feel good about who I am. I feel free to allow you to be who you are, knowing that your success and happiness does not in any way diminish my own. This is a growth and abundance mindset.

I recently stumbled across a quote that jumped off the page for me. It reads:

> *Girls compete with each other. Women empower one another.*
>
> —Unknown

Most of us would not call ourselves "girls" and probably refer to ourselves as women at this point in our lives. But many of us carry inside of us that mean girl, who is nothing more than a wounded part of us that believes she is not enough. When we act from this wounded place, our actions are nothing more than a projection of our own insecurity.

We can choose to instead act from a higher self, a more authentic self, and no longer allow the mean girl to call the shots. We can choose to heal the wounded part of ourselves and lean into the journey of self-love and respect. We can be free of the tyranny of comparison and competition, but it must start with the relationship you have with yourself, and that comes down to awareness.

Often my clients recognize themselves in this particular mindset, but they initially might not see how incredible the impact of shifting their inner dialogue and language is in changing their mindset. Only after they try to stop beating themselves up do they tell me that they never realized how demoralized they previously felt.

THE JERK BOSS SYNDROME

The Jerk Boss Syndrome is a nickname I made up for a phenomenon I see involving self-sabotage with behavior change. It goes hand in hand with the Mean Girl Mindset because the Jerk Boss and the Mean Girl are, metaphorically, one in the same. They are a voice in our head that we don't like, don't respect, and ultimately will end up resisting.

Have you ever worked for someone you didn't like? Perhaps he or she was critical, uncaring, demeaning, or demanding. I bet you have some choice words of what you would like to call that boss (keep that in mind for later).

I want you to think about your job performance under that boss. Did they inspire you or leave you feeling unmotivated? Did you feel encouraged or afraid to take risks for fear of making a mistake? Did you ever feel the need to rebel and take an extra ten-minute break or sneak pens from the supply closet (come on, maybe just the urge . . .)? In what way did working for this boss undermine you? How did it sabotage your ability to do your very best?

Now that you have taken the time to answer those questions, I want you to think about dieting and how you approach most diets. Are you approaching the diet from the mindset of "You are overweight and not good enough as you are, so you better lose this weight, and then you will be good enough"?

If you answered yes, then I have bad news for you. When you try to alter your relationship with food using a critical mindset, you become that choice word you used to describe your boss.

Most people approach changing their eating habits from a place of shame or disgust. Their underlying attitude reeks of "I'm not good enough as I am, so I better change my body so I can finally be okay." This attitude is a setup for failure from the start. It is as though you are being commanded internally by the jerkiest (not yet a diagnostic term, but should be) boss of all time. From the beginning, your motivation and enthusiasm will be tainted. Your connection to the changes you make will be forever colored by the echoes of the nasty boss, and you will feel resentful about them (albeit unconsciously at first).

The bottom line is, if you are approaching change as if you are working for a jerk boss, or if you are your own inner mean girl, you are going to find a way to sabotage something. Fire the old boss and replace her with someone who values you and respects you. You'll see your "performance" improve right away!

ACTION STEPS

1. *Create the Wise Woman*

Awareness of our inner dialogue and self-talk gives us insight into who is running the show.

If you become aware of your inner mean girl, you can choose to reframe and redirect your self-talk. You can create the wise, authentic woman who chooses to be kind, loving, and compassionate to herself. As our awareness grows, we are given the amazing gift of recognizing that we have choices about how we treat ourselves.

- Choose to no longer criticize yourself or other women.
- Choose to no longer compete.
- Choose to no longer compare.
- Choose to embrace and rejoice in the success of other women, and it will free you to embrace and rejoice in your own success.
- Choose to see beauty in all women—including you.

The last bullet can translate into a daily practice that is both easy and exponentially rewarding. I do this often and I can't recommend it enough. As you are going about your day, every time you meet a woman or see a woman who catches your eye, find one thing about her that is beautiful to you. That's it, nothing too complicated. It's simple, but don't mistake that for unimportant. The conscious choice to see women as beautiful creates a ripple effect of change with regard to both your inner and outer life. It changes your mindset, increases self-compassion, and helps you see other women as your sisters instead of your competition.

What I just described is the very literal work of creating a new mindset. I use the word "work" intentionally. We have to choose to think this way, day in and day out, and staying mindful of—and redirecting—our thoughts is hard work! Give yourself some major props for being on this journey, because it is the journey of the warrior. Yes, you. You are stronger than you think.

2. *Pay Attention to Your Language*

Language is extremely powerful. During my work as a therapist, I have become increasingly aware of and interested in the power of our words and the impact they have on our emotions. Language and the words that comprise it are the symbols our intellect has created to describe and explain our experiences.

As we weave our words, we are telling our own brain a story about what our experiences mean. Meaning then translates into how we feel about these experiences. We are literally telling ourselves how to feel with every word we utter. The words we choose to craft the stories we tell are critical pieces of the picture if we want to feel better about our bodies and our relationship with food.

- Focus on thoughts that possess compassion for yourself. Use gentle words like love, appreciate, accept, honor, embrace, and allow.
- Focus on gratitude for your body's function in order to create a mindset of love and respect. Remember that your body has continued working for you despite any possible neglect or abuse. Intentionally choose words of appreciation when thinking about your body, such as love, respect, appreciate, thankful, support, etc.
- Use language you would use with a child, or refuse to say anything to yourself that you wouldn't say to a child. If you aren't particularly drawn to children, then think about someone or something you love and feel protective of.

Perhaps a best friend, parent, or even your dog or cat. Just think about how you speak to the person or animal you deeply love, and use that as a benchmark for how you speak to yourself.

- Be mindful of words that are negatively connotated for you. Sadly, many words that describe our bodies and our biology have been used as weapons in our diet culture. Some women are reclaiming these words (fat, curvy, and thick, to name a few) and using them with intentional positivity as a way of reclaiming their right to be in their body and love it as it is. For others, these words still hold pain and the legacy of ridicule that may have been attached to them. Be mindful of how you relate to language. Only you know how the words you use to describe your body affect your self-worth. Be sure to choose words that make you feel worthy and empowered.

3. *Attach to the Deeper Meaning and Motivation for Choosing Self-Compassion*

Quieting the inner mean girl and choosing self-love isn't something we figure out. It isn't something we learn how to do and cross off our list. Like mindful eating, it's a practice. It is a commitment. It is something we work on daily, as we would a relationship with another person. It is a decision we make every morning when we wake up.

Once we make that decision, however, it creates a ripple effect that goes much further than just the obvious. Yes, deciding to be kind and compassionate to yourself improves your confidence and self-esteem. Yes, it makes your outlook more positive. And yes, it drastically improves your life. But there are other things that happen when we commit to loving and accepting ourselves. Consider this:

- It eases the resistance and suffering that come with disapproving of who we are. When we are free of this conflict, we are free to be our best selves, and this world desperately needs the influence of its most empowered women.
- When you are a happier person, you spread that happiness out into the world.
- When you are accepting of yourself, you unconsciously give others permission to be accepting of themselves.
- When you refuse to give into the critical and judgmental attitudes in our culture, you diffuse the power that they have. When many of us do this, it changes the cultural norm—but it has to start with an individual. You could be the one person who tips the scales. Someone has to be.
- We pass our beliefs and our behaviors onto our children and those people in our lives who look up to us. When we embrace self-love, we teach it to others.

Your decision to love yourself—to embrace kindness and make efforts to quiet the inner mean girl's tyranny—not only changes your life, but it impacts humanity. The ripple effect goes far beyond that which you will ever witness. It's a win-win, with no negative side effects and very little risk. Connecting to this deeper motivation helps you as you commit to change. Again, it is about so much more than the food.

SUMMARY

1. If you are approaching change from a Mean Girl Mindset, you will respond as you do when you are working under any sort of tyranny (such as working for a jerk boss): with rebellion and resistance.
2. We must identify our inner critic—our inner "mean girl"—in order to change our critical mindset into a self-loving mindset.
3. We create a self-loving mindset by:
    i. Creating an inner wise woman who can protect us from our habitual, critical thoughts
    ii. Being mindful of and intentional with our language as we choose to deliberately change our inner dialogue
    iii. Understanding the deeper impact of loving ourselves and treating ourselves with kindness so as to motivate ourselves to embrace self-compassion day in and day out

6

The Rigid Mindset

Everyone's opinions about things change over time. Nothing is constant. Everything changes. And to hold onto some dogged idea forever is a little rigid and maybe naïve.

—Frida Kahlo

Diet Mindset #4: The Rigid Mindset
Type: Inflexible Mindset
Sounds Like: "I have to eat an exact amount of specific food groups and only then will I be okay."
Cause: Rigidity Breaks under Pressure

The principle behind Diet Mindset #4 is that, when under pressure, anything rigid will snap and break. Imagine a dry stick, and think about what happens when you apply pressure against it. Since it is rigid and cannot bend, it snaps in half and is broken.

Just like tangible things can be rigid, so can our behavior and beliefs. When our behavior is rigid, all it takes is a small amount of pressure and our behavior tends to "break." And if you haven't already deduced this, diets—with their rules, numeral limits, and their good/bad food lists—are *very* rigid.

You're either on the diet, or you're not. There is very little room for grey thinking in the traditional Diet Mindsets. Diets are full of dichotomous rules and language: "on/off," "good/bad," "allowed/restricted," "approved/not approved."

Let's look at a client of mine as an example. Claire (pseudonym) came to see me because she had been dieting most of her adult life. She had been yo-yoing in the same cycle for years. She would start her diet on Monday and do really well until about Thursday afternoon, when what she labeled as her "willpower" started to crumble.

She called it a "complete loss of control," and by Thursday evening, she was indulging in forbidden foods. By Friday afternoon she was usually into a full-blown binge. This continued until the following Monday, because, in her words, "I'd completely screwed everything up, so I might as well enjoy it and start over on Monday."

Because Claire started every Monday by going *on* a diet, when the pressure of her job and life caught up to her and she made a choice that was not part of the rigid diet-rule structure, she automatically came *off* the diet. It was all or it was nothing.

Had Claire not been on a diet, she may have been able to mindfully learn from her choices and see how eating past fullness or from deprivation doesn't align with how she wants to relate to food. She might not have gone into the full-blown binge that carried on through the weekend. She might have been able to learn from her choice and her feelings of disappointment, and then decided to be more aware at the next meal. This example is also chock full of the deprivation effect from Diet Mindset #1. It's a double whammy.

Remember the swing effect from Diet Mindset #1, the Deprivation Mindset? The Rigid Mindset is in many ways directly related to Deprivation Mindset, because one activates the other. Rigid thinking activates the feeling of deprivation. The good news here is that as you work on changing the Rigid Mindset, your Deprivation Mindset will automatically become easier to adjust and change.

As we approach change, we have to remember that rigid, inflexible rules don't adapt or adjust to variation (addressed in more detail in Chapter 10: The Bureaucratic Mindset). And change, or variety, is the very nature of our world. Rules just don't have the flexibility to honor the curve balls that life will inevitably throw at us. We live busy lives full of diversity, and that's a good thing! We travel, we have interruptions, and there are days when, from the time we get out of bed to the time we get back in, nothing goes the way we plan.

While this constant flow of choice, change, and chatter we call life is an amazing gift, it can also feel uncertain, overwhelming, and unknown for many of us. It can be scary to be a human being—we are dropped down here from wherever your belief system tells you we came from with no guide book other than the guidance of one or two adults who, if they are being honest, don't really have a clue what they are doing either. Our true reality is the opposite of what we yearn for, which is certainty. Our true reality is uncertain, and as such, like magnets, we can be drawn to rules and beliefs that seem certain because they make us feel safe.

Many people attach to rigid dieting and restrictive eating because it feels like something certain and assured in this chaotic world, thus giving them a false sense of safety in a world that might otherwise overwhelm them. They focus on following rigid rules to avoid having to feel their own feelings. They don't seek their own authority because, in doing so, they must acquiesce to the somewhat scary truth that there is no "external authority." There is just us, imperfect and scared as we are, trying to make the best of an unknown situation we call life.

I have so much empathy for why we sometimes cling to rigid rules for a sense of safety. I have done this very thing much of my life, and I continue to see areas where I have this tendency. I think we all do. If we go back to Diet Mindset #2, the Externalized Mindset, it reminds us that we are trained to look for rules and guidelines outside of ourselves. Rigid, dichotomous rules fit that structure well and give us tangible, measurable ways of knowing if we are being "good" or "bad" little girls or boys.

The truth is, our experience—the very human experience—is not dichotomous. It is not black and white. We want it to be, and man, we certainly do a great job of trying to force our perceptions into those neatly packaged, clean little boxes of certainty. But try as we might, we can't change the nature of things as they are.

My clients will tell you that duality is one of my favorite things to talk about. And no, it is not nearly as geeky and philosophical as it might seem, either! I love to simply point out that it is *impossible*, given the nature of the order of the universe, to have, do, or be anything that does not also include its opposite. Cannot be done. Never gonna happen.

What do I mean? Let nature give you the examples.

Light cannot exist without darkness; spring is always followed by fall, summer inevitably yields to winter; daytime is always followed by nighttime; and you can't be born without experiencing death.

Applied to human nature, psychologists have long talked about the fact that this same duality we see in nature also applies to the experience and range of human emotion.

We all are capable of experiencing duality in emotions:

- We can love someone and yet dislike them at the same time.
- We can be a generally happy person who experiences sadness over a news story.
- We can feel excitement and disappointment at the same time, as is often the case when things end and new things begin.
- We can feel desire and feel disgust all at once.

Our very nature is fluid and complex. We can be happy one moment and fearful the next. To follow rules that never adapt, change, or allow for any movement at all is like asking a fish to function on land. Rigid thinking just doesn't fit the fluid nature of our human experience. And yet we have a tendency to cling to rigid thinking despite the fact that it hurts us. It keeps us small when our nature is to expand. It limits our ability to grow and change, and when it comes to food, rigid thinking definitely plays a role in yo-yo dieting and the restriction-and-binge cycle.

It is up to us to adapt to a more flexible and change-oriented mindset. The following action steps will help you to start doing this today.

ACTION STEPS

1. Create Dialectics

When I say "dialectics," I am referring to a method of examining and discussing opposing ideas in order to find the truth.

The term dialectics became most apparent to me when I learned about **dialectical behavioral therapy**, which has become a gold standard in the treatment of eating disorders. Dialectical behavioral therapy (DBT) teaches individuals mindfulness and skills necessary to help them feel their emotions and tolerate them, while at the same time learning how to manage and adjust their behaviors. The term dialectic is used because the approach pays special attention to the fact that, for all of us, it is possible to hold more than one truth about any one thing, and in knowing this, we are able to seek the balance in all things.

According to DBT's founder, Dr. Marsha Linehan, the term "dialectical" means a synthesis or integration of opposites. The primary dialectic within DBT is between the seemingly opposite strategies of acceptance and change. For example, DBT therapists accept clients as they are while also acknowledging that they need to change in order to reach their goals (Linehan 2008).

With food, an example of a dialectic might be "Go ahead and eat it!" alongside "Pause and be mindful before you eat." It is as though a green light and a red light are both present at the intersection. Beginning to see this as acceptable helps to eliminate dichotomous thinking and assists us in operating from a more balanced perspective. Here are some examples:

- Pizza is both delicious and a favorite food, therefore I am allowed to eat it.
  AND
  Pizza is historically a food I tend to overeat to the point where I feel sick, so I always practice mindful eating and try my best to honor my fullness cues and stop eating when I'm full.
- Chocolate is one of my favorite foods; therefore I won't deny myself this food as an act of self-love.
  AND
  Chocolate is a food I have a complex history with, and I still have some old mindsets about it that

might be lurking in my subconscious that cause me to feel guilt or hide my choice from others. Because of this, when I eat chocolate, I take my time and really enjoy the experience, allowing myself to experience the pleasure inherent in eating. I do not have to eat it fast; I can savor the experience.

- I give myself permission to eat whatever I want as a way to heal my Deprivation Mindset and give my brain the message that food is in abundance.
  AND
  While all foods are permissible, I choose to be mindful of how I eat them. I choose to listen for signals as to when I reach fullness, choosing to honor my body as best I can by listening to its cues.

When you practice seeking the dialectic in all things, you will begin to automatically find the middle or grey zone in things. You create a moderate guideline internally, putting you back in charge, instead of the old scenario where the rules were in charge. This type of thinking lends itself to being more compassionate in general, as you are seeking "both sides of the story." This is also a much gentler and kinder approach to change, as it honors our complexity and nonlinear nature. It can help you deepen the changes you make moving away from the Mean Girl Mindset we discussed in chapter 5.

2. Avoid the Perfectionism Trap

So many diets and efforts to create a healthier life start out well, but without realizing it, we sabotage our success by creating rigid rules for change instead of establishing compassionate intentions. The difference between the two hinges on one major issue—**the Perfectionism Trap**.

I honestly can't tell you how many times I fell into this trap before I realized what exactly what going on. For example, I would set some goal such as "I am going to stop procrastinating," expecting that I would go from being someone who procrastinates one day to suddenly being someone who never procrastinates the next. I set the intention as though something magical was going to happen overnight that would teach me everything I needed to know to stop procrastinating. That's like picking up a guitar for the first time and expecting that you are going to play like Eric Clapton. Let's face it—it's not going to happen! It is an absolutely unreasonable thing to ask of ourselves, and yet that is often our approach with dieting.

"As of Monday, I am no longer eating high calories or fat" was the battle cry of every woman of my generation as we set out to finally conquer the food enemy *du jour* (because it changes every decade or so). Nowadays, it seems the common cry is "As of Monday, I am no longer eating sugar or carbs." But the fundamental problem remains the same. You can't expect to change a long-standing behavior overnight. You didn't create it in a day, and you won't change it in a day either. (It's important to note here that when I say "change a long-standing behavior," I am using this behavioral example to explain the erroneous belief that change should be immediate inherent in the perfectionism trap. Do not misinterpret this as saying that you *should* be changing this long-standing behavior or be attempting to cut out food groups. I hope by now you realize that is the opposite of what you should do; this particular example is just wrought with erroneous Diet Mindsets.)

Many of us can white-knuckle our way through change for a brief period. However, without really learning new skills or gathering the experience necessary for true change, we give up at some point, usually during our first "less than perfect" moment, when we feel like we have failed. That's why dieting is so destructive and such a setup from the start—the entire structure of a diet is built around the all-or-nothing thinking inherent in perfectionism.

Rather than set unrealistic and often self-defeating goals, I suggest you work with compassionate intentions to avoid the Perfectionism Trap.

- Who do you want to be?
- How do you want to feel?
- What burdens would you like to part with?
- What new experiences would you like to have?

Notice the questions above are more about connecting with your inner wisdom than they are defining your worth based on an external standard. That is exactly the point. The difference between setting goals based on compassion and setting goals aiming for perfectionistic outcomes is that when you are using compassion, there is room for exploration, whereas with perfectionism, you either meet the goal or you fail.

A rigid perfectionistic goal sounds like "I must be a certain number on the scale in order to be attractive." A compassionate intention is "I want to feel confident and comfortable in my skin. What kind of things do I already do that make me feel that way?" (Note to self: do more of these things!)

I want to share with you some examples of intentions that are designed to help you heal your relationship with your body and reprogram the unhealthy perfectionism you adhere to. These intentions can be used daily in an effort to change the inner dialogue. If you are practicing the action step of creating the inner wise woman from chapter 5, these intentions would be directly in line with something she would say. They are about compassion, not perfection.

- I choose to be kind to my body. I show my body love and support by listening to its messages and doing my best to respect its needs.
- I choose to see myself as perfectly imperfect. I am a work in progress, ever-changing, ever-growing, and ever-adapting. I am wildly, messily, and amazingly human, and I choose to remember that when otherwise I would want to judge myself.
- I choose to focus on my character instead of obsessing over my body. I see aspects of my character—such as being kind, funny, brave, creative, talented, smart, or compassionate—as a huge part of my worth, in addition to my outer shell. I am both body and soul, and I choose to reflect on the balance of both.
- I intend to choose foods that nurture and heal my body. I will be kind to myself when, and if, I fall into old habits, and I will remember that every moment is an opportunity to make another loving choice.

Do you notice how gentle these intentions are? That's the point. Gentle and compassionate intention setting gives you room to grow and learn. It embraces the flexible and balanced approach to thinking that is known to give you better results.

And for those type A folks out there freaking out at the thought of moving away from high-pressure goal setting, this isn't about allowing yourself to slack off. It is simply about allowing for times when you don't quite hit the mark, which is allowing for life to happen, because that is the nature of change. There is no such thing as perfection. It doesn't exist.

Our world often tells us to push harder and strive for more. That's fine, if that appeals to you. It isn't for me to tell anyone exactly how they should approach their life. Set goals; strive to be your best. I only ask that you consider the nature of change. Change occurs through trial and error, not overnight.

You can choose to start using the intentions I gave you or create some new ones for yourself. Just remember that this is an action step, so you must actually say these things to yourself. You can do this out loud, or simply read the intention to yourself. It works best if you memorize them so that you can repeat them to yourself throughout the day. If we aren't changing our thoughts, there are plenty of marketers and mean girls out there who will be perfectly willing to do it for us, so choose wisely.

Just remember, in setting your intentions and goals, focusing on balance will allow you the flexibility to ride out the unavoidable learning curve that comes with change. Be compassionate, be loving, and most of all, be persistent. You are worth it.

3. Eat a Grey Meal

This intervention is more about sending a signal to yourself than it is about the meal. Have you ever heard the saying "actions speak louder than words"? It's a common saying for a reason. Our behavior is always sending a message to our brain about what is and is not acceptable. No matter how fastidiously we work on changing our mindset and inner dialogue, if our behavior doesn't back up our new belief system, the changes won't stick.

In this action step, I want you to identify certain foods that in the past—in your old, fixed Diet Mindset—you identified as either "good" or "bad." Most of us do this when we are using rigid, dichotomous approaches to dieting. But even if you don't have a set list in your head, it is likely you have a sense of what has and has not been allowed in terms of eating in the past. This is the list I want you to draw from.

At one meal this week, I want you to combine those two foods, one from the "good" list and one from the "bad" list.

The point is to experience balance. I am not suggesting you do anything that is not in keeping with your desires. Don't eat anything unless you genuinely can feel good about it. I simply want you to have a meal that is neither good nor bad (based on the old rules), but rather, a bit of both. Choosing this meal and incorporating grey meals into your everyday life challenges your old Rigid Mindset and helps create a new, less rigid way of being with food.

This sends a powerful message to your brain that experiencing dialectics with food is possible. It also tells your brain that you are now making the choices about food, and the external rules are no longer in charge. This meal is an act of rebellion against the Rigid Mindset and the Externalized Mindset, and it silently tells the Mean Girl Mindset that the rules are changing, so she better get on board with the program.

SUMMARY

1. When under pressure, anything rigid will break.

2. Our thoughts, like things, can be rigid. When life applies pressure, our behavior "breaks," which leads to the dichotomous swing of all-or-nothing behavior.
3. Like nature itself, human nature is dual, which means we must be flexible in order to flow with life, rather than resist it.
4. Being flexible and adapting allows us to learn from our mistakes and avoid the all-or-nothing behavior trap. We can do this by:
    i. Practicing dialectic thinking
    ii. Avoiding the Perfectionism Trap
    iii. Practicing eating grey meals

7

The ABC Mindset

Repetition is not failure. Ask the waves, ask the leaves, ask the wind.

—Mark Nepo, *The Book of Awakening*

Diet Mindset #5: The ABC Mindset
Type: Linear Mindset
Sounds Like: "If I diet, I can lose weight, and then my life will be perfect."
Cause: The Belief That Change Is Linear

In my practice as a therapist, I have had multiple sessions in which clients came to me distraught because they had found themselves struggling with old issues that they thought they had dealt with or cured. Many people have the notion that once something is addressed, it is done with.

This is something that happens often. Clients become excited and engaged upon seeing change and making strides toward their goals, only to become angry or pessimistic upon running into a roadblock or having to deal with their issues again. They feel like this means they are failing.

If I have learned anything in the work I do, it is that change is not linear. You don't start off at some point in time labeled "bad," work your way up to "better," only to one day move up to "perfect" and stay there.

Life isn't linear. We want it to be. We try to believe it is. But it isn't.

Life revolves around cycles. Again, we must only look at nature to see this: the earth's cycle as it orbits the moon, the seasons, the ocean tides, our menstrual cycles, the life cycle of a human itself. Around and around, back and forth, ebb and flow.

For what appears to be such a dominant energy cycle, it interests me that a lot of humans have a strong desire to do it differently. We seem to be intent on moving "up" or forward (in a linear direction). We only value forward or linear movement, and we seem to be set on avoiding certain aspects of whatever cycle we are in that we label as "bad."

Think about the way we structure our organizations. For the most part they are hierarchies, with a direct line that you can rise up or move forward on, starting at entry level and going all the way up to CEO. Our grading system is linear as well: F is bad, D is better, C is even better, B is pretty good, and A is great. This is why I chose to call this mindset the ABC Mindset. It's something we have all experienced and can relate to.

I can go on and on, giving you example after example, but the main idea is simply to understand that society has taught us to look at the world in a "bad, better, best" type of line. It is the collectively accepted consciousness of our culture. So if you see yourself in this type of thinking—it's okay. We all tend to think this way; it is how we are raised.

And yet, the catch is this: It *simply isn't true* when it comes to change.

Because our world has adopted a linear, hierarchical structure, people believe that change itself is linear. People think we start at a fixed point and that we move away from that point directly toward our goal. This is *the biggest* fallacy out there (change is not linear, quite the contrary—we will get to that soon), yet we come by this belief honestly due to our conditioning.

There are two different ways of looking at the change process that use metaphor and imagery to help us connect to a deeper understanding of the process. They are **the Spiral of Change** and **the Labyrinth.**

Both of these metaphors/images will allow you to reconnect with your own change process and start to understand what is really happening along your journey. What you once perceived as failure will now be seen as progress. What once might have thrown you off of your course will now be understood as simply part of the process.

Buckle up and get ready—it's time to paradigm shift.

THE SPIRAL OF CHANGE

Imagine that you are at the bottom of a spiral staircase.

Now, I'm going to introduce a basic symbol for something you want to eliminate or remove from your life. The symbol is a trash can, and as you stand at the bottom of the staircase, you look at the trash can, and it is an eyesore. It also smells, and you want to get as far away from it as possible. In order to do this, you begin to climb a set of spiral stairs that offer you an escape from the smelly trash can.

You climb up and up, going around and around, and when you get to the third floor, you look down, and much to your chagrin, you can still see the trash can. It is smaller than when you were on the ground floor, but it's still there. You can also still smell it; however, the smell is a little more tolerable as it is fainter than it was when you were right next to it.

So you continue to climb, and you continue to spiral up and up until you reach the fifteenth floor. Here, you look down, and that darn trash can is still there. This time, however, you notice it doesn't bother you as much. It is smaller and less irritating. You also notice the smell is barely noticeable at this point.

You can continue the metaphor as long as you need, climbing to the one hundredth floor, and as you can imagine, making the view and the smell of the trash can on the first floor minuscule and barely noticeable. This metaphor demonstrates a truth about change that linear thinking doesn't: we don't remove the obstacles from our lives entirely. They remain as we change, but our perspective on them changes, the way our perspective changes as we view the trash can from ascending viewpoints.

As you grow and change (going up), the things you are trying to change don't immediately disappear (the trash can). Change is like climbing a spiral staircase. As you go up, you will continue to see the same thing over and over again if you look at a fixed point as you peek over the guardrail. Though you will be seeing the same thing, each time you rise up a level, it will appear to be a little different. The truth is, the fixed point hasn't changed, but *you* have.

You are in a different place; therefore, your perspective is different. As you climb, each level you reach will give you a new level of perspective. Eventually, once you climb high enough, you will no longer be able to see that fixed point. But that comes with time and with the persistence in climbing. Just because you continue to see that fixed point doesn't mean you aren't making progress.

If we apply this metaphor to changing our relationship with food, it would speak to the fact that as you change, you are likely going to see the same patterns that you are trying to heal—repetitively. This doesn't mean you aren't making progress!

Let me repeat: experiencing struggle no longer means you are failing. From now on, it is simply part of the process!

Each time you see these patterns repeating, ask yourself:

- How am I different this time?
- How did I react differently?
- What felt different this time?
- What did I learn that I want to avoid next time? (Because on the spiral, there is probably going to be a next time.)

The spiral of change doesn't just allow for "mistakes." Rather, they are necessary parts of the climb. They teach us *how* to be better, do better, and react better.

So remember, just because you see old patterns from time to time doesn't mean you aren't changing. You are. You are just climbing the spiral staircase.

THE LABYRINTH

In her book *Eating in the Light of the Moon*, Anita Johnston, PhD, says this about the process of change:

> The women on the road to recovery from disordered eating began with a journey that required them to follow a twisting, turning, winding path to their centers. It required them to leave behind old perceptions of themselves that they had adopted from others and to reclaim their own inner authorities. They had to listen to the voice from within to give them guidance and support as they searched for their true

> thoughts, feelings, and desires. They found themselves letting go of all expectation of linear progress, disengaging the rational mind, and embracing the power of their emotions and intuition. (Johnston 2001, 9)

Eating in the Light of the Moon taught me a wonderful metaphor for change. In the book, it talks about the change process, and describes the process of healing your relationship with food as a labyrinth.

In general usage, labyrinth is often synonymous with maze, but there is actually a distinction between the two: *Maze* refers to a complex series of branches, a puzzle with choices of path and direction; while a *labyrinth* has only a single, nonbranching path, which leads to the center.

The idea is that when you start your journey of change, you enter the labyrinth. The road has many twists and turns and is anything but linear. You might feel like you are starting back where you came from, and yet you are still working your way to your goal, which is the center. In our case, the center is your authentic self—your soul, your spirit. You are journeying back home, back to the core of who you really are.

The twists and turns in the process appear on the surface as "behavior change." But the real process of change—the real prize—is reconnecting with your center.

The lesson from the labyrinth is that you should not mistake a hairpin turn in your road for failure or distress. If you journey back around and see something similar to what you saw in the past, you can trust that this is part of the necessary twisting and turning as you work your way to your own center.

As long as you are willing to commit to staying in the labyrinth (i.e. staying committed to showing up for yourself with awareness and the intention to keep trying), you will arrive at the center. *There is only one path.*

Your old patterns of behavior may continue to cycle in and out, but each time you are able to approach them differently. The change is not occurring on the outside; *it is occurring within you.* The change occurs in your thinking and your beliefs about the problem. The labyrinth itself never changes to help make your journey get easier; *you* learn from the labyrinth, from the frustrations and the process of getting lost. The struggle of figuring the twists and the turns of the labyrinth teaches us, changes us.

If you have a moment when you engage in old behaviors that are aligned with an old Diet Mindset, remember: change happens when you choose to respond to your perceived failure with kindness instead of judgment. Change happens when you decide that it is not failure, but rather a part of the change cycle, and as a result you are able to calmly go back your new mindset in a balanced way.

ACTION STEPS

1. Call a Truce with Failure

Your old beliefs have been there a long time. It will take time to reprogram, and that is okay. Changing your mindset is a process, not a one-and-done occurrence. Say it with me, say it out loud—*it takes time!*

If you find yourself thinking diet thoughts, wanting to restrict, or harboring old thoughts of judgment or body hate, don't *try* to not think them. Trying NOT to think a thought is like me telling you NOT to think of a pink elephant. See, it's impossible—you thought of a pink elephant, didn't you? An emergence of your old beliefs or thoughts isn't a sign of failure; it is just a sign that change takes time.

The whole idea of failure versus success is part of the old paradigm. It is linear thinking; it's a fixed mindset. Rewriting your inner narrative around what failure really means is the first step to seeing change differently.

For much of my life, I waited only until I knew things were perfect, or that I would present as perfect, before I would act or let the world see who I was. Needless to say, in order to do this, I missed a lot of opportunities. I played small when I knew deep down I was far more capable, and I silenced my voice when I always knew I had something to say.

I can still remember my "aha" moment, when this started to shift for me. It's a moment I won't easily forget. I went to a conference years ago, and Sara Blakely, the CEO and founder of Spanx, was in the audience. She was pulled up on stage and asked to talk for a minute, and the story she told has stuck with me ever since.

She told the audience that when growing up, her parents had a ritual at dinnertime where she and her brother would report their day's events. Part of the ritual was sharing all the things they had done in which they had failed.

The interesting thing was, talking about their failure was something they were *excited* to do. They saw it as a game, and they would even compete to see who did *better* at failure that day. She and her brother would take pride in sharing their failures during gym class, with their schoolwork, and with friends. With joy, they would report their failure, and in turn would receive beaming smiles of pride from their parents, who would validate them and cheer them on, encouraging them to continue on and fail some more.

Failure was exciting. It was fun. Her parents managed to make failure something that felt like success.

Her parents taught them at an early age that failing was something that was, in a word, awesome. It meant that they were trying, because the only way you can fail at something is to first try something new. Failure was accepted as a natural part of this process and as an indicator that they were out there trying new things. No guilt, no shame, no personalization. Failure was an indicator of success, merely a sign of their attempts.

I remember being blown away by this story as I sat in the audience. It was one of those lump-in-throat-water-in-eyes moments. It was so simple, yet so unbelievably brilliant. Her parents had managed to teach them their own meaning of failure, and they'd stripped it of all the shame and blame that so many of us learned to associate with the word.

I could see the image of two little kids beaming with pride while talking about failure, and it gave me goose bumps. I remember thinking, *Oh my god, it is really that simple? Is it possible to reclaim the way we look at things?*

Sara went on to explain that when she became inspired to empty her bank account to support her dream of making pantyhose with the feet cut out of them a real business venture (which she shared even *she* thought might be a little crazy), she never worried about failing. Had she feared failure, she never would have followed a dream that so many people told her was insane.

We all know the ending of this story. And if you don't, I can sum it up in one sentence. Sara has taken Spanx from a one-product business to a billion-dollar enterprise.

I think about this story a lot. Every time I fear failure (and yes, that is still quite often; like most of us, I too was indoctrinated to fear failure), I think about those little kids sitting around the kitchen table laughing and feeling excited to report their failings.I have consciously and deliberately decided to reclaim my own meaning of the word failure, and lay this out before me every time I tiptoe out of my comfort zone.

There is a saying that reads, "Don't die with your music still inside of you." By reframing the meaning of the word failure, I know one thing for certain: that my music is playing. Reclaim the concept of failure as something that shows you are on the journey of intentional living, and shift out of your ABC Mindset.

2. Host a Meet and Greet with the Itty-Bitty-Shitty Committee

When you hear the old negative voices (I once heard these voices referred to as the "itty-bitty-shitty committee" in your head), instead of fearing them, get to know them. By engaging these thoughts, you begin to see what you might be able to learn from them. Allow them to exist, knowing that they are part of the cycle of change too. They are part of the lesson, not evidence that you are not succeeding.

Stepping into a new and healthy relationship with food involves bringing with you *all* parts of who you have been up until this point in time. That means *all* of your old thinking and behavior is coming along for the ride. So when you see it show up, don't be surprised it's there. The next time you run into old beliefs, be kind and say, "Of course you're here. Why wouldn't you be?"

Instead of running from the committee, respond.

- "What do you need from me?"

- "What do you have to teach me?"
- "What are you afraid of?"

These are all great questions to start off with. Look at them as icebreaker questions as you start to get to know the inner critical voices that have plagued you. You don't have to act on what they say (and shouldn't, as we established earlier in the book—the inner mean girl often says abusive things), but you also don't have to run. Under the negativity and fear is often a genuine need and something that needs to be understood.

Instead of just blindly responding, next time, create a counter voice (this goes hand in hand with the creation of the inner wise woman). If the itty-bitty-shitty committee says, "You shouldn't be eating pizza," instead of just feeling guilty and taking those words as truth, respond this time. Say, "I can eat pizza when I want to because I'm not buying into the Diet Mindset anymore, so calm down. The rules have changed. It's okay to eat what I want. Is there something bothering me? Could there be feelings hidden underneath my fear of food?"

If we can learn to no longer fear and to respond to our critical thoughts, we can learn from them. When the voice told you not to eat the pizza, it might have actually been trying to tell you that you were feeling insecure. Often, the fear of food is masking a deeper fear. What you may have needed in that moment was reassurance that you were all right and that you were not going to be judged by your own inner critic.

Much of our journey is spent in relation to our inner dialogue. Listening to the old voices of pain and learning how to create new, empowered messages about who we want to be and what we choose to believe is a huge part of reclaiming our body image and self-worth, and of carving the path for a truly internalized and authentic relationship with food. In essence, we are rewriting the narrative that plays alongside our lives (I always think of the adult Kevin's voice from *The Wonder Years* when I think of this).

3. *Embrace Repetition*

Repetition is part of the process. I mentioned earlier in the book that repetition is one of the foundational ways in which we learn anything. When you embrace repetition, you move through it and beyond. When you resist repetition, you experience frustration, and that can lead to sabotage or quitting.

When you see the same problems resurface, focus on the ways in which you are thinking, feeling, or behaving differently in the face of this old issue. Focus on your inevitable wisdom and growth in the face of these challenges.

This sounds simple, but that doesn't mean it's easy. I recommend if you start judging repetition as failure, take out a pen and paper (or your phone and open the notes app) and begin a list of all the ways you did it differently this time. Doing the list will force your brain to really search for the answers, and it will focus your attention on the presence of change, rather than the presence of the remains of old habits.

The story about Thomas Edison and the invention of the lightbulb summarizes this best. Apparently, he tried thousands of times before the invention finally worked. The point is, however, that he never gave up. Edison tapped into his tenacity and belief in himself as he tirelessly worked toward bringing his invention to fruition. He chose a growth mindset and reframed the process by embracing the repetition of change instead of seeing it as a linear concept flanked by success and failure on either end.

> *I have not failed. I've just found ten thousand ways that won't work.*
>
> —Thomas Edison

Instead of seeing repetition as a sign of being stuck or a lack of progress, embrace repetition as evidence that you are a strong and tenacious warrior committed to creating your best life.

SUMMARY

1. Change is not a linear process, but rather a process full of twists and turns that enhance your experience and teach you the lessons necessary for the change you are trying to achieve.
2. Your journey of change is an internal process where you change your perspective and acquire wisdom, as opposed to an external process where external variables change.
3. Failure is a linear, dichotomous-mindset concept. When looked at through a nonlinear, compassionate mindset, however, the concept of failure becomes evidence that we are changing, growing, and actively living our lives. In other words, the old concept of failure is now a badge of honor, signifying that you are indeed courageous and strong.
4. Embracing the inner critic, rather than trying to escape it, allows you to learn from your behaviors rather than react to them or avoid them.
5. Embracing repetition as evidence of success begins to undo the linear mindset and establishes a new growth mindset that embraces a natural part of the nonlinear-change process.

8

The Take-an-Aspirin Mindset

The problem is never the problem. It is only a symptom of something much deeper.

—Virginia Satir

Diet Mindset #6: The Take-an-Aspirin Mindset
Type: Quick-Fix Mindset
Sounds Like: "My problem is I can't stop eating. If I could only stop eating food, everything would be okay."
Cause: Treating the Symptom, Not the Problem

Imagine going to see the doctor with a broken arm and having them tell you to just take an aspirin and move on. Would you trust your doctor? Would you believe their advice?

Hopefully not! Hopefully, you would feel outraged, or at least confused. You would wonder why they weren't setting the bone and addressing the cause of your pain. I hope you would get a second opinion and take matters into your own hands.

Going on a diet to lose weight is very much like taking an aspirin to treat a broken arm. It erroneously looks at weight as the problem; it colludes with the oppressive notion that our bodies are the problem instead of really identifying the destructive cultural and political forces that are behind the beliefs in the first place.

People reading this book are likely in different situations and different body sizes. Living under the negative influence of a (or many) Diet Mindset(s) manifests differently within everyone, and looking at someone and their body can never, ever tell you the true story of their experience. That is why it is so helpful to let go of the Take-an-Aspirin Mindset and start to look deeper.

It is important at this time that I make a clear statement about mistaking weight as "the problem." Weight is not and never will be a behavior or a thought, therefore it cannot be the issue. And (this is really important that you hear this clearly) many people who are in larger bodies are perfectly happy and healthy despite all the cultural oppression they are forced to deal with.

The health-at-every-size (HAES) movement aligns nicely with the ideas behind why we must end the Diet Mindset. The way I summarize HAES is that it suggests that if we focus on our health, and take the focus off of weight (which is intentionally negatively framed to keep women in "their place" in a society that benefits from oppression and the consumer reflex to buy products to fix perceived bodily imperfections), then our choices are going to take our bodies to a place where they are happiest. This may include weight loss for some bodies, and it might not include weight loss for others. But if our choices with food and movement are balanced, and our resulting doctors physicals, our lab results, our stress levels, and our subjective feeling of wellness all align with our standards for healthy living, then isn't that what is really important? Body weight is not and never will be directly correlated with these outcomes. If you don't believe me (don't judge yourself if you don't, as we are culturally hypnotized to believe that fat is the enemy), and if you want to see the research that I am referring to, I encourage you to read the book *Health at Every Size* by Linda Bacon, PhD, in the reference section. Even the strongest cultural hypnosis can't deny science and research outcomes, and her book is full of both that support the idea that physical health and body weight are not necessarily directly correlated. HAES encourages all people in all body sizes to focus on making their bodies as healthy as they can; it just does so in a way that doesn't make weight or weight loss the primary indicator and emphasis of health itself.

Therefore, as you read this chapter, it's really important that you hear that I am in no way suggesting that everyone who lives in a bigger body has some deep-seated psychological issue to deal with. I do not believe this to be the case at all. Many people who live in bigger bodies live contently in their bodies and have full and amazing lives. Many people have larger bodies simply due to genetics, cultural eating habits, and life choices. None of these things are inherently problematic until our culture or an outside influence tells us that they are. This is where our cultural conditioning becomes a problem.

Our cultural norm for the ideal body shape for women is so skewed and unhealthy that many people think their body size is too large, when in fact, it is healthy and perfect for their genetic makeup. The concept of an internalized "set point" theorizes that everyone has an ideal body size that will manifest when they eat in balance with their body's hunger/fullness cues. Unfortunately, for many women, this "set point" feels too large, and they continue to diet and engage in unhealthy restriction in an effort to make their body smaller than it wants to be. It is important here to emphasize that if maintaining a body size requires that you restrict your food intake and ignore your hunger cues, it is likely that your body size is not your body's actual ideal healthy body size, but rather it is a size you are clinging to because of our culture's unhealthy standards.

Dieting in order to fix the perception that your body is too large to be acceptable is just like taking an aspirin to treat a broken arm. It focuses on addressing pain, but it isn't addressing where that pain is coming from.

You cannot just continue to look at the symptom; you must address the underlying problem. Taking a deep look at the reason you dislike your body is necessary in order to truly change the Take-an-Aspirin Mindset. This mindset is about getting to the core of self-loathing and self-rejection that our cultural body-image norms have fostered within us. Our bodies are not the problem; our culture that promotes hatred of the curves of a women's body is the problem.

We live in a patriarchal world. I could (and might just yet, give me time) write an entire book on how this affects the way women relate to food. But for the sake of this lesson, and brevity, I just want to point out here that in a world where the patriarchal structure needs women to believe that they are lesser-than and not worthy in order to maintain the dominance of men, it makes sense to tell women in order to be deserving, they must be unhealthy. The thin ideal requires that we engage in behavior that destroys our bodies, our minds, and our souls. This is completely by design. In order to maintain this ideal, we must devote excessive energy and time to manipulate our bodies, and in doing so, we weaken our bodies, minds, and sources of strength. We unwittingly distract ourselves and weaken our power, so as to create an entire gender of people who are not only easier to oppress (by virtue of our buy-in to the belief that we aren't okay as we are), but too tired, downtrodden, and hungry to even have the energy to do something about it. Your body has never been the problem; it has been the target of a system of oppression that has been around for centuries. It's time we awaken to the truth and refuse to play along with those who do not have our best interest in mind.

On the other hand, I do see cases where people use food to self-medicate and numb their emotions. I see people who feel compelled by their relationship with food and feel that they are in an out-of-control cycle with eating. I see cases where people replace love or relationships with food.

There are also plenty of cases of people who are just constantly on a diet. They are constantly yo-yo dieting, going back and forth from restriction to overeating, losing and gaining weight in a constant and never-ending cycle. It is the cycle, the living in the dichotomous extremes, that is the problem here—again, not the weight.

What is important here is that you start to focus on why you are in pain, and not just try to eradicate the pain by shoving your body into a box that society has deemed the norm. The pain you experience when you break your arm is necessary. It is a message your body sends to you to make damn sure you are going to treat the real problem: the break in the bone. If you numb the pain, you might avoid the important part of its message: do something to fix the problem! If you don't set the bone properly, it might heal in a way that makes it hard for that part of your body to function. This is analogous to what happens so often when women try to numb their pain by dieting; the real problems go ignored and get worse over time.

Consider the following questions as you reflect on your own relationship with food and the deeper motivation behind your choices.

- Do you struggle to love and accept your body's natural size because it doesn't fit the societal ideal?
- Are you convinced that your weight is the problem when actually the culture you live in and the way it has conditioned you to hate your body might actually be the real issue?
- Do you struggle with creating a balanced relationship with food due to messages you have received about how much you should eat or what you should eat?
- Are you using food to numb or disconnect?
- Do you rely on food as your best friend?
- Does food equal love?
- Is food the one thing in your life that you feel like you can control?
- Is food the one way in which you know you can get a reward—when the things you really want seem unattainable or out of reach?
- Have you just always been on a diet because, well, that's what everyone else does?
- Does dieting just seem like the normal way to relate to food and your body?
- Are you maybe just a victim of our Diet Mindset culture, and never knew there was another way to relate to food?

Take a deep pause and really reflect on these questions. See where you relate. Remember, we aren't linear, dichotomous creatures, so your answer may not be clear, but rather mixed and with shades of grey. That's okay. The idea here is to seek your inner wisdom about what is really lurking beneath the food habits and body-image issues that are hurting you.

We are emotional creatures (yes, all of us!), and we experience our lives on an emotional level. Our culture has become increasingly dependent on the intellect to explain every minuscule area of our lives, but despite our best efforts, our emotions are still there. They can be a mystery to many of us, but they are a driving force for our behaviors whether we like it or not.

Our emotions, and the subsequent emotional needs that arise as a result of being a human being, are often overlooked, ignored, or many times unknown. We are left hungry, even starving for our deeper needs to be met, but because we are so cut off from understanding our true hunger and the true cause of our symptoms, we know nothing better than to feed our stomach with food. We misread the signals.

NEEDS OF THE SOUL

Did you know your soul needs feeding? Is it a new notion to even wonder if it is possible to have something such as a hungry soul? Have you ever even considered the notion that hunger is something that goes much deeper than the physical desire for food?

I believe that hunger is a way of describing the experience we have when our body/mind/soul is telling us that there is a need we must meet.

When our body needs feeding, we experience the physical hunger for food. When our soul needs feeding, we experience the deeper hunger for *more*.

Often, due to the fact that very few of us are educated around the deeper needs of the soul and therefore are honestly unaware of the process, we misunderstand soul hunger and its signals. We mistake soul hunger for physical hunger. It happens all the time.

Let's take a minute to explore the deeper needs of our soul, and how these needs are vital to the overall health and well-being of every single human being. Underneath the everyday, tangible needs we have (like food, clothing, and a roof over our heads), we have deeper needs that can't be seen or touched but that are equally as important.

What are some of the needs of the soul? The needs of the soul are the yearnings that will nag at you no matter how you try to quiet them or avoid them. Respect, autonomy, play, love, creativity, validation, and inspiration are all examples of "higher-order" needs that feed your soul on a deeper level.

But here's the thing: our souls, amazing and tenacious as they are, are relentless in their desire to help you achieve your own personal best. The soul does not stop talking to you, urging you on to be, do, and experience your very best, despite whatever roadblocks you may be experiencing.

This is why, regardless of how oblivious or unable we are to heed the calling of our self-actualization, we are always feeling the hunger for something more. Something better. This is why, though we are sometimes so in denial (which is a loose acronym for "don't even know I am lying") about our soul hunger that we honestly mistake it for physical hunger, there is no amount of food that will ever—ever—satisfy our desires.

This doesn't just apply to people who "eat their feelings" or overeat. This same concept affects those who restrict their food or are constantly dieting. Feeling this deep hunger leaves people feeling needy. This feeling of neediness at times can feel out of control and all-consuming. People turn to restriction or dieting as a way of attempting to control and subdue this feeling of hunger because they don't know how else to calm it.

Why are we in denial about our soul needs? How is it that we become stuck and unable to recognize what we are really hungering for? We ignore the urging of soul hunger for many reasons, including (but certainly not limited to):

- We don't believe we are worthy.
- We don't know how to get what we desire.
- We believe our needs are not important.
- We fear our desires are somehow wrong or immoral.
- We fear failure.
- We have been taught that denying our needs is prudent or responsible.
- We fear rejection if we admit our truth.
- We are focused on the needs of others and don't have time for our needs.
- We have been taught it is loving and nice to sacrifice our needs for the needs of others, or, conversely, that to focus on our own needs is selfish.
- We have been taught to suppress our desires.
- We are ashamed of having needs or being needy.
- We don't believe we are safe in this world, and therefore we spend all of our resources defending ourselves, which blocks us from receiving.
- We honestly didn't know that our soul had needs—no one ever talked to us about it, and the concept is entirely new to us.

The good news is this constant yearning for more (that oftentimes manifests as physical hunger) very well might be your soul screaming its head off to be noticed. I tell clients that they should really thank the part of themselves that has eaten to excess or dieted to deprivation, not because the tactics used were good ones, but rather because that part of us (or "ego state" as I like to call it) has been fighting like hell to get your needs met. It was just going about it in the wrong way.

The feel-good takeaway? The soul will never stop trying to help you see that you are worth more. It's a tenacious and spunky chick who will fight for you; you just have to make sure she has the tools to do so in a way that helps you instead of hurts you.

ACTION STEPS

1. *Become a Food Detective*

In order to change the Take-an-Aspirin Mindset and to really start to get to the bottom of what is fueling your current relationship with food, it is important that you explore why you use food. Keep in mind that when I say "use food," that could mean eating too much, dieting, or severe restriction. My experience has taught me that overeating and not eating are two sides of the same coin.

Why do you think you use food to cope? Your reason can be anything—as long as it resonates as truth to you. Our reasons are varied. Let me give you a couple of examples of common triggers for emotional eating or restriction.

Some people have lost connection with themselves, busy in their lives taking care of everyone else's needs but their own. They use food to comfort themselves and numb the feelings of sadness at being lost and no longer a priority in their own life.

Some people use food to feel in control of something in their life because everything else feels so out of control. Usually this shows up as excessive dieting and fear of food. The belief is, if I can control the outside (my weight), I can "fix" the inside (fearful or difficult emotions), which is never true.

Some people control their food because they have bought into the cultural oppression that tells them their body is wrong as it is. Question this notion. Is that actually true? Have you been hypnotized your whole life to believe you have to fix your body when in fact, it might be perfectly healthy and normal as it is? Are you a victim of cultural oppression and mind control?

Some people use food because it was the way they were shown love in their family. They came to know food as their friend, a constant that they could turn to when life became overwhelming. It's so common to use food to demonstrate love or calm emotion. Think about the classic lollipop given to a child after a doctor's visit to calm the child's fears. Food feels like comfort. And often, food feels like love.

The reasons we use food are countless. Listen to your story. You can use your journal in this action step and write down the patterns that you become aware of. The more you understand where the root of the symptom is, the closer to identifying the underlying cause you get.

Okay, so now that you have your detective's hat on, let's go even deeper. In order to do this, you can use the following action step to gather more info for the story.

2. Notice Your Parallel Patterns

I have made an observation doing the work that I do, and

I have a hypothesis as a result. Here, in my oh-so-scientific terms, I'm going to lay it out for you:

How you do anything is how you do everything.

That's right. I truly believe that we have patterns of behavior—or as I like to call them, energy patterns—that show up all across the various categories of our life. For instance, someone who tends to overeat might notice that they also tend to overspend, overcommit, overdisclose, and lack boundaries in most areas of their life. While helpful, focusing on one specific thing—food, money, relationships, etc.—doesn't exactly get to the root of the problem. We must look at the energy pattern that lies underneath all the similar behaviors.

This is not exactly a complicated idea, and yet it is pretty cutting edge within the scope of accepted ideas about changing our relationship with food. To tell someone that the number of items on their to-do list, their spending habits, or the clutter that is scattered all over their home may be related to their compulsive eating is not discussed in your typical diet book.

If we are constantly taking on more than we can handle and feeling burdened by the minutiae in our lives, is it any wonder that those negative feelings lead to negative choices? Oftentimes, the very weight we carry in our lives is the trigger for our emotional eating. It's an endless cycle.

This concept is predicated around my pretty simplified hypothesis: how we do anything is how we do everything. And this is just a hypothesis; it is a statement of curiosity that is intended to guide exploration and research. I know that no one statement is going to be true for every single circumstance in human behavior, but for the sake of getting to the deeper roots of your relationship with food, I want you to keep that detective hat on and investigate how this could be true in your own life.

If you have a tendency to overeat, eat compulsively, or binge eat, consider the following:

- How does having a to-do list a mile long make you feel?
- What emotion does a laundry room that is so full you can hardly close the door evoke in you?
- How do you feel when you are trying to get something done surrounded by clutter and mess?
- What are your predominant emotions when you are doing the work of three people?
- Do you ever feel out of control with spending, in relationships, or in managing your life?
- How does it feel to carry too much weight in your life?

The same idea applies to the other side of this spectrum. If you have historically been a rigid dieter or you have engaged in restrictive eating, you might notice that you don't embrace life in a full enough way. It's likely your own boundaries for many things in your life are as rigid as your eating habits have been. Perhaps it's time you start staying yes to life a little more, as you start saying yes to food a little more. Consider the following questions:

- Are there areas of your life you wish were different, perhaps more alive or exciting?

- How do you feel about new relationships? What is it like for you to be vulnerable and not feel in control?
- What is your relationship to cleaning like—do you require structure or perfection in your environment in order to function?
- What is your relationship to work like—are you rigid and perfectionist in your demands?
- How do you relate to money? Are you afraid to spend or are you strict with your spending?
- How might your relationship to other people, friends, or partners, be full of restrictions or rules that parallel how you relate to food?

3. *Environmental Control*

You wanna fly, you got to give up the shit that weighs you down.

—Toni Morrison, *Song of Solomon*

Toni says it best. "Stuff" weighs us down. It weighs down your heart, and it weighs down your soul.

What form can "stuff" show up in, and how do we know when we have *consumed too much*? (Pay attention to how this language can be directly used to describe overeating.) I believe that our stuff can show up as almost anything we feel we have too much of or feel overwhelmed by—therefore, you are going to have to chime in as the expert of your own life.

That being true, there are some basic categories that I want to encourage you to start thinking about. These areas of life can be the places you start your search for where you are carrying excess or being too rigid and controlling and not allowing yourself to receive (the two opposing manifestations of this same issue).

Either in your journal or with a highlighter, identify those areas that resonate with you as being areas you want to work on, and then make a plan for slowly changing the dynamic within this category. The more changes you make in your environment, the more your relationship with food and body image will change, because, you guessed it, how you do anything is how you do everything.

Your External Environment

This is your tangible world, which includes your home and all the "stuff" you have in it. It includes your car, your purse, your office, and your desk or any creative space you work in. It is any place you claim as yours and visit frequently. If this includes other places, like family members' homes or group meeting places, you can include these.

Your Relationships

This is obvious on the surface, but we aren't just making a list of all the people and groups we call friends and family. We are looking at the obligations we have and the roles we play in these relationships. It is an examination of where we have taken on more than we can handle. This can be your relationship with the PTA or your relationship with your homeowners association. It can be anything.

Within the scope of relationships, we also want to look at where we may be carrying another person's weight (i.e. taking responsibility for other's feelings, trying to fix other people's problems, or taking care of other people when that is something they are able to do for themselves) at the expense of our own self-care.

This of course includes systems, such as family, work, and organizations. We are in relationship with larger systems just as we are in relationship with individual people.

Your To-Do List

This can be the list on your fridge, but it also needs to include the constant list you have running around in your mind. This is the never-ending diatribe of "I should" and "I need to" that you can't quite seem to make a dent in.

Your Habits

Here we examine things that we are doing that are no longer serving us but we carry them around anyway. Smoking, drinking too much, and obvious "bad" habits would fit here. There are also other, less obvious habits that weigh us down, for example: complaining, judging, whining, gossiping, lying, and manipulating. These are all examples of less obvious habits that, when out of alignment with our authentic self, can be a heavy burden on us. When looking into our habits, we are looking for the excess we carry for no other reason than we've always done it.

The first step is to examine these areas of your life. Identify the behaviors and the energy patterns that are out of balance and perhaps mirror your relationship with food. The next step is to take each area of imbalance that you have identified and give it an action step.

So, if you notice your spending is out of control, and that you avoid opening your credit card bills each month (similar to your overeating and avoidance of yourself), meeting with a financial planner or making a budget becomes an action item. If you notice you cut off friendships at the first sign of conflict (similar to the way you cut out any food group that scares you), then your first action item is to call the friend you've been avoiding and ask her out for coffee.

These insights you are developing about the parallels between how we relate to food and other areas of our life give us a lot to consider. You don't have to change everything at once. If you feel overwhelmed by all of the new awareness, and the change that comes with it, I really recommend you get help and allow someone to assist you navigate this journey with you. None of us have to go this alone. It is one step at a time, but you must realize where change has to be made beyond just looking at food in order to truly change your Take-an-Aspirin Mindset.

SUMMARY

1. Oftentimes, the problem as we see it (our need to control our weight) is not really the problem at all, but rather it is a symptom of a deeper problem.
2. This deeper problem is likely associated with an emotional need that is not being met.
3. We must learn what our emotional needs are and then begin to explore ways of making sure these needs are being met if we truly want to address our deeper soul hunger.
4. Three ways to do this are as follows:
    i. Become a food detective, and write down the clues you find while examining your relationship with food.
    ii. Notice your parallel patterns. How you do anything is how you do everything, so pay attention to patterns and tendencies you notice with your behavior in general. It will give you insight into why you relate to food the way you do.

iii. Start to change your dynamic with your surroundings, which includes your external environment, your relationships, your to-do list, and your habits.

9

The Playing Small Mindset

There is no passion to be found playing small—in settling for a life that is less than the one you are capable of living.

—Nelson Mandela

Diet Mindset #7: The Playing Small Mindset
Type: Fear-Based Mindset
Sounds Like: "I'm not sure, what do you think?" (when you actually have an opinion)
Cause: Cultural Beliefs and Fear of Being Too Much/Not Enough

Diets are all about reducing choices, limiting options, and staying within the lines. Like I said earlier in the book, I am not speaking out against nutritional information or guidance, but I am honing in on the psychological ramifications of living your entire life dieting, restricting, or obsessing about food or living in fear of food because you feel you can't stop eating it.

I named this chapter's mindset the Playing Small Mindset because I want to highlight that living a life on a diet is like constantly being told to tone it down, be quiet, and know your place. This mindset is inherent in traditional dieting processes.

The very essence of dieting is restriction. Restricting something is to lessen it or to make it smaller. This, and dieting itself, plays along nicely with the societal belief that has been held for many years about being a woman.

It's not news to any of you that women spend an inordinate amount of time trying to make their bodies smaller. We want our thighs slimmer, our hips narrower, and our tummies flatter. We want the number on the scale to be smaller. We want our dress size to shrink. The message is clear: smaller is better. No doubt about it.

Psychology 101 teaches that one of the most powerful forms of teaching is modeling. In a world where the literal model that a woman sees portrayed as "ideal" is often a size 00 (because a 0 isn't small enough?), is it any surprise that women subconsciously fear taking up too much space?

I know from my own experiences with dieting that smaller was always better. It wasn't really stated overtly, but it was very much understood. I had that message reflected back to me by peers, media, and the general cultural norm. In other words, it wasn't just me.

Since that time, I've experienced this phenomenon with many of the women I have helped. They come to me afraid of their own desires, wants, and needs. Many of them are so used to ignoring their own hunger that it never dawns on them that they have the right, let alone the necessity, to feed their hunger and put their own needs first.

Is it any wonder that many women also struggle to take up space in their own lives?

Taking up space in your life means being willing to claim your space at the table (more parallel food language—I love this stuff!). It means that you recognize that you have a voice, an opinion, needs, wants, and desires that all matter equally to the voices, opinions, needs, wants, and desires of anyone in your life.

Unfortunately, I hear this type of thinking all too often:

- I don't want to be a burden.
- I don't want to trouble them/you.
- I don't want to be high maintenance.
- I don't want to upset anyone.
- I don't want to cause conflict.
- I don't want to inconvenience anyone.

The truth is, I still to this day have to work around these thoughts all the time. I'm still moving my way up the spiral staircase and still see/hear these smelly trash-can thoughts from time to time. My social conditioning has taught me to be such a "nice" girl that every time I speak out against something I am offended by, or refuse to acquiesce to another's beliefs, I still experience a sense of fear. The difference today as compared to when I lived by these rules, however, is that the fear is accompanied by other, more dominant emotions. The Wise Woman I created internally guides me to feel determined to speak out, proud of my opinion and defiant against rules that would have me believe I don't matter because of gender or size. The fear I feel is there, but it is overruled by determination, pride, and defiance. And at the end of the day, the Wise Woman is there to offer compassion and reassurance if fear starts to mess with me.

Underneath our tendency to play small, there is often the basic fear: "I am afraid that I am too much." The twin sister of that fear is the opposite fear: "I am afraid that I am not enough." These fears are born of the same place. It is a fear that there is something wrong with us as we are, and so we shrink ourselves, our bodies and our desires, lest we reveal to the world that which we fear may be defective.

Our bodies and our lives are inextricably linked. We cannot pretend that they don't parallel one another. When someone feels good about their body, their self-esteem increases. When someone feels healthy and energetic, they feel more motivated to engage in their own life. In world where we are encouraged to chase the dangerous dream of making our body be a size 0, is it any surprise that women are too comfortable playing small and letting someone else claim the space that might rightly be theirs?

Well, I'm here to ask you, what is *too much* anyway? What is *not enough*? Who defines this number? Does an objective truth for this measure really exist?

Our lives, and all of our needs, are meant to take up space. Our bodies—our beautiful and sacred bodies—were designed to take up space.

I believe each of us is born with an equal right to an equal amount. Outside of obvious oppressive social forces, what we end up with sometimes has a lot to do with what we believe we deserve. Please question whether you might be following the false belief that you are supposed to play small. It isn't serving you or the world.

Marianne Williamson, author of *A Return to Love*, says it best:

> Our deepest fear is not that we are inadequate. Our deepest fear is that we are powerful beyond measure.

> It is our light, not our darkness, that most frightens us. We ask ourselves, Who am I to be brilliant, gorgeous, talented, fabulous? Actually, who are you *not* to be? (Williamson 2012, 191)

ACTION STEPS

1. Pay Attention to Body Language—Try the Superwoman Pose

Have you ever paid attention to your body language? It's not a common thing for people to put their attention on, and yet studies show that body language plays a role in self-confidence, self-efficacy (your belief in your ability to accomplish specific tasks), and physical health.

Women are often twisting themselves into pretzels. In an effort to stay small and take up as little space as possible, it is not uncommon that women hold more guarded poses, such as crossing their arms and legs. Just look at the difference in the way men and women sit on an airplane.

Amy Cuddy is a researcher at Harvard University who studies body language and the impact it has on your hormones. Cuddy and her research team have classified different body positions as "high-power" or "low-power" poses. In general, the high-power poses are open and relaxed, while the low-power poses are closed and guarded.

Cuddy ran an experiment in which people were directed to pose in high-power and low-power poses, assigned randomly, for two minutes. They're then given the opportunity to gamble—since people in high status are found to be more risk tolerant (and less responsive to stress).

When the researchers looked at the results, the results showed something pretty amazing. In both human and nonhuman primates, expansive, open postures reflect high-power positions, and closed postures reflect low power. Not only do these postures reflect power, they also produce it; in contrast to adopting low-power poses, adopting high-power poses increases explicit and implicit feelings of power and dominance, risk-taking behavior, action orientation, pain tolerance, and testosterone (the dominance hormone), while reducing stress, anxiety, and cortisol (Cuddy et al. 2012).

No, this one pose isn't going to change your old Playing Small Mindset overnight, but it is an easy and user-friendly exercise that takes two minutes and that no one can lament is "hard." Just stand in the superwoman pose: You simply stand tall, legs firmly planted hip width apart, with your chest out and your hands on your hips.

Do it right now, in fact. Okay, I'm waiting . . .

Felt kind of good, right? Pay attention to your body and embrace open postures as often as you can. Send the message to your body and to your soul that you are committed to reclaiming your space in the world.

2. Learn to Receive

One tendency a lot of my clients demonstrate is that they have a very hard time receiving.

They have a hard time asking for help and an even more difficult time receiving it. They cannot receive a compliment and feel uncomfortable when people say nice things to or about them. They have a tendency to feel like they are a burden to others if they need or want things. They do not want to inconvenience anyone, and God forbid they cause any sort of conflict or problem for someone else. They simply cannot receive the act of someone else giving them their time, attention, or emotional energy.

The act of receiving is an incredibly important part of living in balance. If all you do is give to others, you are going to deplete your own stores of time and energy. This is especially important for the givers of the world: the caretakers, the parents, and all the sensitive people who respond to the needs of the world.

The best analogy for this is one that many people are familiar with, and that is the oxygen mask on the airplane. We all know that when traveling, the safety guideline for using the oxygen mask is that you must place the mask on yourself before you assist a child or anyone else with theirs. This is so that you are awake, breathing, and alive in order to help others. You need the mask *first* to assure you will be okay, and *then and only then* are you able to really help those around you. The oxygen in the airplane is analogous to your time, attention, and energy in life.

If you can't receive, then you may not literally die the way you would without oxygen, but parts of you feel dead because you have given everything away without replenishing your own needs. You may feel tired or fatigued, overwhelmed, burnt out, resentful, or just empty. It is impossible to thrive without receiving.

The way out of this habit of refusing to receive is to begin to look for opportunities to receive every single day. It might be helpful to start small, so as not to overwhelm yourself.

- When someone opens the door for you, receive their help. Look them in the eye and say, "Thanks!"

- When the bagger at the grocery store offers to help you to your car, say yes, and do not apologize or make excuses for allowing them to help you.
- If someone compliments you, simply say "Thank you," and shut your mouth before you have a chance to downplay or deflect their comment with some "Oh, this old thing?" type of statement.
- When anyone offers to do anything for you, before you automatically say "No, I'm fine," just say yes. Practice saying yes, over and over.

Learning to be comfortable with receiving help, and taking up the figurative space in your life, also sends a message to your mind and soul that it is your right to receive, and this translates to food. It connects with your right to receive pleasure from food, as receiving anything at all is an act of nurturing yourself.

These seemingly simple acts of accepting help from others adds to the overall inertia of change that you are creating by adapting your new abundance mindsets around food. The statement that each act of receiving makes is "I am worthy of receiving," which over time translates to a new mindset as you approach anything in life, including food.

3. Define "Enough"

Recently, I went to the mall to return something, and upon leaving through the large anchor store, I "ran into" a sales rack of blue jeans.

Okay, let me take a pause for a second and explain something: I am a blue jeans connoisseur. If I could wear jeans every day of my life I would (and for the most part I do). I have refined my love for jeans to an art, and I have my very favorite brands that I have come to love through a long process of trial and error.

Yes, my relationship with blue jeans is a long and sordid one, and as a result, I have a closet full of them—and I mean *FULL* of jeans. I have dark fade and light fade, skinny and stretchy, ripped and tailored, boot cut and straight leg. I have enough blue jeans to last me through the next decade.

So there I was at the store, mesmerized by these beautiful jeans. They were my favorite brand—the one with the ridiculously long name that means absolutely nothing—and the equally ridiculous price tag. And yet, this amazing pair was on sale for fifty dollars.

Fifty dollars?? the voice in my head screamed. *That is unheard of! You cannot walk away from these. You must have them!*

Had they been food, I would have been salivating.

I had them in my hand, when I remembered a Facebook status update that I had read earlier in the week from Geneen Roth, author of *Women, Food and God*.

She posted:

"I keep having to remember that enough isn't a quantity. It's a relationship to what I already have."

The truth is, I have enough jeans. Really, I have more than enough. I need a new pair of jeans like I need a hole in my head. There, I said it.

Another truth is that I will probably always be tempted by what I want, which is the new, bright, shiny object. I want what I want when I want it. Don't we all on some level?

But what happens when we keep acquiring? What happens when we never connect to the feeling of "enough"?

If we don't recognize the feeling of being full, or of having enough, we are constantly in search of, or seeking, something outside of ourselves to fill us up. We are on a never-ending wild-goose chase.

With food, the process is much the same as it is with blue jeans. You can eat and eat and never recognize that you are full. You take in more than you need. You consume more than you actually have room for, and there are consequences.

As I stood there with those jeans in my hand, I took a moment to center and get conscious. (Yes, I do this stuff. I practice everything I preach!) I asked myself, *Do you need another pair of jeans? Really?* Very quickly the answer came: *No, think about what you already have—think about how full your closet is.*

As I did this—I mean, I really thought about all of the jeans in my closet—I started to feel grateful and full. I realized that I have enough. I didn't just think it; I felt it. I felt the feeling of having enough. (And this is huge, because "enough" isn't just a thought—it's a feeling.)

I put the jeans back on the rack and walked away. Now, I get that I'm talking about shopping. Not exactly deep stuff here, right? But the jeans and the story are just a simple symbol for the process that plays out for many of us in life, in our energy patterns (remember the *how you do anything is how you do everything* hypothesis?), and with food.

With compulsive dieting and restriction, the feeling of never being enough is quite present, but it shows up in an inverse way, through an attempt to control the world and the inner emotional state by never needing anything, not even food. We try to control our need for consumption. It is an effort to assert our will over our needs so as to prove to ourselves, and the world on some unconscious level, that we don't need anything, so we can't be hurt by not being good enough or needing too much.

Compulsive overeating is about never feeling that you have had enough, and consuming so much you feel sick, bloated, and emotionally out of control. The things you consume end up consuming you.

Bulimia (binging on food and purging it through vomiting, laxative use, or compulsive exercising) is about feeling that you can't possibly have enough, so you consume exponential amounts, only to feel so overwhelmed by the overconsumption that you must purge yourself of everything you have taken in. This process leaves you again feeling empty—primed to repeat the cycle.

And it doesn't have to just be about food. As this chapter attempts to highlight, we have a relationship with everything we connect with, and that relationship tells a story about who we are and how we see the world and our place in it. Remember, our relationship with food probably parallels our relationship with other things in our lives, opening up a gateway into insight if we are courageous enough to explore.

I like my stuff. I like acquiring. I'm human and I love playing in the amazing playground that is life on this planet—with all the beautiful things and the abundant options we have. But I also know the feeling of overconsumption, and I know the consequences of not knowing when I am way beyond full. There is a middle ground somewhere in there that is uniquely placed for all of us. I'll buy another pair of jeans at some point. (Editorial note: In fact, I have bought another pair since originally writing this. Remember, this is not about perfection. This is about awareness.)

I am grateful for the reminder that "enough" comes from connecting to what I already have. It feels calm and centered, as opposed to the urgent, needy feeling that comes with chasing the carrot that cannot be caught when you try to find the feeling of enough outside of yourself.

So, I encourage you to start a practice of mindfulness around being really aware of what you already have a sufficient amount of. Be mindful with food, material things, or emotional experiences. Ask yourself: in what areas of your life are you already full? Where are you aware of the feeling of sufficiency or fullness? The more you begin to connect with this feeling, the better able you'll be to recognize being full on a physical level and with regard to having met your need for satisfaction with food.

SUMMARY

1. The Playing Small Diet Mindset is all about restricting, reducing choices, limiting options, and staying within the lines. Consistently living by the rules of this mindset sends a clear message about our worth, or lack thereof. It creates a world where the belief "I must not take up too much space" becomes the norm.
2. The fear of taking up space is predicated around the fear of "enough-ness"—not being enough, or being too much. It is a fear that if we express our needs, it is going to cause us to, in some way, become rejected and hurt, either because we aren't worthy of having our needs met or because our needs are going to be "too much" for someone else to handle.
3. We can change our mindset to be more confident and compassionate by learning to take up more space with our physical bodies and postures, by practicing deliberate receiving throughout our day, and by becoming mindful of and therefore defining for ourselves the feeling of "enough-ness."

10

The Bureaucratic Mindset

Dieting is a $33 billion-a-year industry. It is based on the idea that most people like to be told what to do, especially when it comes to food. That's part of the lure of diets: they make people feel like children again, because they tell us that we cannot be trusted to handle food; that we are not capable of making up our own minds and having control over how we eat.

—Geneen Roth, An Interview on Mindful Eating, *The Sun*, January 2002

Diet Mindset #8: The Bureaucratic Mindset
Type: Dependent Mindset
Sounds Like: "Even though I want to eat this, and it makes sense to eat this, I can't—because it is not on my diet."
Cause: Following Rules without Questioning Their Efficacy

Bureaucracy is often defined as the administrative system governing any large group. In this case, I want you to look at the diet industry as this administrative governing system. I also ask that you look beyond the definition of the word, focusing more on the typical frustration people have with bureaucracies.

Bureaucracies are often criticized for their inflexibility, inefficiency, and unnecessary complexity. They are also criticized for being so big that they are out of touch with the specific needs of their individual citizens and for relying on rules that are in place to keep order but that do not necessarily serve each individual in each situation.

Here's a great example of how the bureaucratic tendency to rely on the rule and not examine the individual situation prevents progress. Many years ago, I was visiting a dear friend from college who happened to work for the government. She shared a story with me that sums up the downside of bureaucracy in the most beautiful way.

While she was working for the US Department of Transportation, she was asked to apply for a promotion in another agency within the department. The two people who asked her to apply were the hiring manager and the human resources director of the agency. She was (at least in their minds) a perfect fit for the job, and they very much wanted her to fill the role.

One of the requirements for the new position—GS-15 in federal bureaucrat terms—was to have at least one year of experience in the next lower position, GS-14. At the time of her application, she had been in a GS-14 role for almost two years. However, when she filled in the online application, she made a typo for the start year of her current job and the result was that it appeared on the application as if she had less than one year of experience as a GS-14. Despite the fact that she clearly HAD BEEN a GS-14 for almost two years, the human resources director (yes, the woman who wanted her for the job) disqualified her application. She was concerned that if my friend got the job despite the typo, it would appear as if she had shown favoritism. Rules are rules, and the application she submitted stated she was not qualified, even though everyone involved knew that was a mistake. *No one got what they wanted!*

Like my friend's story, when you function from a set of bureaucratic rules, you often end up losing opportunities, making poor choices, and completely missing your needs in the moment because you are following an external rule that has no ability to think for itself and no idea of what the actual situation is.

Imagine that you are following a specific diet that requires you to eliminate bread. You are doing so with the Bureaucratic Mindset that the rules are the rules, regardless of the situation or specific needs of the individual (in this case, you). Week three on the diet and your job requires you to go to San Francisco for a conference. In addition to being the land of Rice-a-Roni (the San Francisco treat!), San Francisco also happens to be known for the very best sourdough bread in the world. I'm talking manna-from-Heaven good.

So here you are, diligently following your no-bread diet, drooling and yearning for a taste of the delicious, chewy, mouthwateringly scrumptious bread, but you are afraid to have a piece for fear of violating the rules.

We are so used to the Bureaucratic Mindset of traditional dieting that we either deny our needs and the opportunity to learn flexibility and balance, or we give in to our needs. But, in order to do so, we feel as though we have to buck the system entirely. This translates into "I can't do this diet anymore," which manifests into an all-out vacation binge, because somewhere in the back of our mind we know that as soon as we get home we are going to start all over again (probably on a Monday) with deprivation.

Diets do not have the ability to think for themselves. The typical Bureaucratic Diet Mindset demands that you follow rules that have no ability to change, shift, and adapt as the environment (i.e. your life!) changes. Even most "flexible diets" are not designed to adjust to big changes such as vacations, illness, injury, etc. The bureaucratic rules these diets set up do not adjust as you adjust, which causes you to miss the opportunity for growth in the moment. This concept of bureaucratic thinking aligns closely with the Rigid Mindset we discussed in chapter 6.

Why would you rely on a rule that you knew deep down didn't make sense when you have the ultimate intelligence within you? In order to change, we must tap into switching from an externalized focus to a more internalized focus (what we discussed in chapter 4). We are the source of our wisdom. Follow the action steps below for ideas on how to turn inside for the answers and reconnect with your own authority.

ACTION STEPS

1. Discover Your Authentic Appetite

We are going to create an artificial moment in order to help you reconnect to your ultimate authority and intelligence when it comes to making food choices—your body.

Your body has so many amazing functions inherent in its complex design, all of which strategically communicate with you regarding what you eat and how you eat it. You are the decision maker from now on, so in order to buck the system and break away from bureaucratic thinking, you have to start getting to know yourself and your body's signals with regard to food.

This starts with discovering your authentic appetite through mindfulness. We discussed mindful eating earlier in the book, and this exercise is a continuation of that process. This exercise is practiced all around the world as a mindfulness exercise, and it requires you slow down to a snail's pace to truly hone in on the moment and magnify your senses.

Ready to play?

You will need to procure an almond or a raisin. We basically just want to work with something small and textured, so yes, a walnut or other similar food item is fine. Sit down with your journal, a pen, and your nut/raisin. Place the nut/raisin on your tongue, but don't eat it. Your goal here is to just be aware of the food item on your tongue. Roll it around. Pay attention to what is going on not only in your mouth, but also in your mind.

- Can you feel the texture?
- How does it taste?
- Do you smell anything?
- What thoughts are running through your mind as you do this?
- Most importantly, how do you feel?

When I do this exercise with clients in workshops, they are amazed at the emotions that come up for them. Many people feel frustrated at not being able to chew the raisin. Others feel irritable but don't know why. Some people feel uncomfortable. Others are amazed at how much they haven't paid attention to food in the past and feel excited.

The key is to be mindful. Do not eat it; just be with it. After a few minutes, you can eat it or remove it, after which is the time to just write down what you experienced. This exercise is about paying attention to your thoughts—not judging them or editing them, but just observing them.

Your thoughts that arise during this exercise will tell you a lot about how you relate to food in general. For instance, were you bored? Were you judging the experience? Were you critical, or were you interested and curious? Was it fun?

We want to use mindfulness to create a relationship with food that is fun and playful and full of gratitude and confidence in our choices, so what you learn here will give you an idea of what is under the surface and what you need to be aware of. This exercise gives you access into your own feelings and helps you reconnect to the source of your authority over your decisions—which is you.

2. Pretend You Are the Boss of the World

When my sister was younger and I wanted her to do something, she often refused. We had the love/hate kind of relationship that only a close pair of sisters could have. She would always tell me, "You're not the boss of the world!" and then flatly refuse to listen to me or my demands.

I always laugh when I think of her comeback . . . but today it sparks for me the basis of this journaling exercise. What if there were a boss of the world, and what if it were you? What if you could write the rules—for anything and everything? What would you do? What would the rules be? What would you change?

This exercise takes getting past your left-brain reasoning and engaging your imagination. Let your inner child have fun with this one. When you get to the end, it might just give you an idea of how you may have conformed to the "rules" simply because they were the norm, and not because you agree with them. And let's just be clear, I'm talking about societal norms—not laws! I'm not suggesting you go rob a bank because you feel like having more money.

I'll give you a simple, silly example:

If I were the boss of the world, blue jeans would be appropriate attire for any occasion. Yes, I'm talking about jeans again. I wasn't kidding when I said I love blue jeans. So if I were the big boss, the blue jean would be the new ball gown.

Now, does this new revelation mean I am going to actually wear blue jeans to a formal event? No. But it does tell me how I am most comfortable. It gives me insight into who I am and the fact that I'm most comfortable being an informal person. I don't like putting on costumes, and I don't like putting on airs. The point is, this exercise gives me that internal wisdom that you can't receive from following a set of bureaucratic rules. And it did inform a decision; when I began working for myself, I decided blue jeans were appropriate work attire when and if I wanted. It's not for everybody, but it works for me.

So what rules would you create if you were boss of the world? The sky is the limit here; have fun with this one. Your inner wise woman might have a thing or two to teach you if you let her start talking. The more you know about yourself, the more informed you are on your soul's needs, and the better you will be in making decisions regarding how to feed yourself.

3. Learn to Sit with Your Own Feelings

Years ago, a dear friend and teacher was helping me with a situation that had me feeling a lot of anxiety. I came to him wanting to know what I could do to make the anxiety go away, and he smiled that gentle but somewhat humorous smile you see when you know you are about to be told something you don't want to hear. He simply said, "Just sit with your feelings; don't fix them." I remember thinking, *Are you kidding me? You want me to just sit with the feeling of anxiety and just breathe?*

This was an idea that, at the time, made me want to run out of the room screaming. I no more wanted to "sit with" that feeling than I wanted a root canal performed without anesthesia.

The surprising truth that came from my reluctant foray into the world of mindfulness—or "sitting with it"—is that after the initial fear and discomfort wore off, there was a great sense of empowerment that came with knowing that I can stay present and grounded despite my emotional urges.

Being mindful with food often requires us to sit with cravings and choose not to act on them. If we want to get our own answers, instead of relying on bureaucratic thinking to tell us what to do, we must remain present to receive these answers from ourselves. We ask questions of ourselves, such as:

- What feelings might have triggered this?
- Is there something else I could do right now that might feel good?
- Can I walk away and come back to this in half an hour and see if I am still hungry?
- How will I feel if I eat that? How will my body feel? Will there be an emotional hangover?
- If I eat this, will I feel good about it afterward?
- How can I eat this and feel good about it?

Do you notice something about all of the questions? They are all directed toward yourself. In mindfulness, we are placing our mind's attention inward, thus signaling to our mind that we (not some bigger bureaucratic source of authority) are the source of the answers we seek.

Consistent practice and repetition of mindful curiosity any time you are in contact with food will, over time, replace the old Bureaucratic Mindset. It will teach your mind to look within for the answer, redirecting your source of authority from the outside system back to your infinitely more intelligent and wise self. Remember, in all things, there is only one authority on what you need, and that is you.

SUMMARY

1. Bureaucratic thinking does not benefit anyone. Never follow a rule just because it is a rule. Use critical thinking and consider the present circumstances.
2. When you connect to your authentic appetite, you realize that your desires and needs change from day to day. Being flexible allows you to move through life with more ease.
3. In order to replace bureaucratic thinking, it is critical that you get in touch with your own thoughts and feelings. If you are going to be the expert on what and when to eat, you must start listening to yourself.

11

The Shame-Based Mindset

Shame is the most powerful emotion. It's the fear that we're not good enough.

—Brené Brown, *Daring Greatly*

Diet Mindset #9: The Shame-Based Mindset
Type: A Saboteur (or Self-Destructive) Mindset
Sounds Like: "Successfully completing this diet will make me acceptable and loveable."
Cause: Dieting *Feels* Terrible

There is an aspect of dieting that doesn't get talked about often. It's the dark underbelly—a silent side effect of dieting—that is as harmful (if not potentially more damaging) as all of the other harmful aspects of dieting: diets breed shame.

Traditional dieting with the Shame-Based Mindset is predicated around the idea that something is wrong and needs to be fixed. This is a self-destructive mindset because it is built on the belief that we are not good enough as we are, which, if you look back on Brené Brown's statement at the start of the chapter, is the foundation of shame.

So here you have it, folks. Traditional dieting is built on shame. That's like building a home on an oozing, festering swamp filled with quicksand and sinkholes. It is doomed from the start, due to the fact that it stems from dysfunction.

From this "not good enough" belief, we are sucked right into the shame cycle before we even realize what is going on. The next thing we know, we aren't really being authentic because dieting causes us to live a lie.

I remember when I was in high school, at the peak of my most disordered eating. I was so obsessed with rigid dieting that I was literally hungry all the time. There was a day that I remember well, where I played hooky from school just so I could stay home and eat. I ate all day long. I was that hungry and that desperate.

Did I tell anyone? Did anyone have any clue? Of course not!

On the outside I looked like the all-American high school girl. I was polite and sweet and caring. I followed the rules and dressed the part. I looked one way on the outside, but on the inside, my food restriction, constant hunger, and accompanying food obsession were preventing me from really living. Dieting and food restriction were my prison, and shame was my warden.

The point is, we never—ever—tell the truth about what our diets do to us. We all walk around admitting only to the "good" days. We look at each other, envying one another's highlight reel, unaware of the truth of who we all really are.

We might laugh at the rom-com films that make jokes about women being hungry all the time. We probably lament the desire to taste the cupcakes we see as we pass by the bakery department with our peers, bonding over how "good" we are when we pass them up and keep moving.

We make sarcastic comments with our girlfriends about how it sucks to constantly have the food police (ourselves) watching over our shoulder. We smile through the frustration. We laugh instead of cry.

But no one caught up in a yo-yo diet cycle is laughing on the inside, because it isn't funny and it certainly isn't fun. No one is really talking about the pain involved. It's not socially acceptable to start a casual conversation with "Did I ever tell you about the time I stayed home from school just so I could eat?"

Shame keeps us trapped in isolation. We are so afraid that if we admit the truth about how we really feel, the rest of the world will reject us and see us as not good enough. Oh, wait! Wasn't that the problem in the first place? Isn't that the core belief that fuels a diet to start with?

You see, shame creates a cycle that keeps us stuck. In order to change our relationship with food, we must change our relationship with shame. The good news is that every single mindset shift and action step in this book is designed in some way to help you change your relationship with shame, as they are all built on a foundation of compassion and balance.

The next three action steps will also help you shift away from the negative shame cycle and start to live in a way that supports your worth and right to exist and take up space in the world.

ACTION STEPS

1. Focus on How You Want to Feel When You Reach Your Destination

For everything you have ever wanted in your life, there was a deeper desire. The "thing" you want is only a surface-level desire. What we really want is the feeling that the acquisition brings us. We are, all of us, always chasing a feeling in every waking moment.

- Do you want more money? It is likely because it will allow you to feel safe or free.
- Do you want a better relationship? It is likely because it will allow you to feel loved or respected.
- Do you want that new shirt you saw at Nordstrom? It is likely because it will make you feel sassy or beautiful when you wear it.

I am in no way qualified to tell you how these things will actually make you feel, so of course, I'm guessing based on my own experience. But the point here is that our real motivation for everything we do is how we want to feel as a result of doing that thing.

When we desire to lose weight or to heal our relationship with food, it is because of how this change in our life will make us feel. It isn't the number on the scale or the shape of our body, but how these things will change our opinion of ourselves, and thus change our feeling state.

Discovering what you are really seeking—the feeling state—is critical.

Stop for a moment now, close your eyes, and imagine you have manifested the intentions you have for yourself that brought you to be reading this book. How do you FEEL? Take your journal and create the header "FEELINGS," and write your feelings down.

These feelings are what you are really seeking—this is the key point to remember. It isn't about weight or food. It is about how you feel, and this is something you can only get in your mind, never by changing the outside.

Now, I want you to stop and look at the feelings you have written down. What are other activities, things, or behaviors that also bring about these feelings for you? For example, if you listed "relaxed" as one of your feeling words, you may discover that another way in which you feel relaxed is taking time to slow down and read a book with no distractions.

Now, take out your journal, and list as many things as possible that bring you the same feelings as those you identified you wanted to feel as a result of reading this book. So, for example it might look like this:

FEELINGS I DESIRE TO FEEL WHEN I QUIT DIETING

- Relaxed—reading a book in silence, meditating, sitting by water, petting my dog
- Free—riding my bike, going out with my girlfriends, writing
- Joyful—being with family, playing with my nephew and niece, watching comedies, playing games

This week, I want you to choose three of the things you listed above and schedule time on your calendar to do these things. This is a nonnegotiable.

You will not half-ass this or do it last minute. It is going to be a YOU priority. It is an important date you are making with yourself. The journey must be filled with the feeling that you are hoping to feel at the end of the destination. This is why diets predicated on the Shame-Based Mindset are self-destructive. The journey is full of nothing but negative feelings!

Approaching your relationship with food from the Shame-Based Mindset doesn't feel good—quite the contrary. It leaves you bruised and weary, with your willpower and self-esteem barely intact by the time they are done. The journey was excruciating and difficult. That can NEVER bring you to a destination that is peaceful and joyful.

Danielle LaPorte, a popular blogger and author of *The Desire Map*, states it wonderfully in a quote from her blog that reads, "If liberation is a chore, it's not really liberation. You can't contract your way to freedom. You can't punish your way to joy. You can't fight your way to inner peace. The journey has to feel the way you want the destination to feel."

2. Rewrite Your Story

Each morning provides us with the opportunity to start a new chapter in the story that is our life. We have this amazing opportunity to decide to do it differently. It doesn't matter what your story has been, today you can start anew.

This seems too easy to be true, right?

What is important to remember is that it is possible . . . but not always easy. Possible and easy don't always go hand in hand, but it is a choice we have as to which of the two we put our focus on. This is one of my favorite quotes:

> *I'm not telling you it is going to be easy. I'm telling you it's going to be worth it.*
>
> —Anonymous

I know this sounds overly simplified, but we must pay attention to what we are telling ourselves about our experiences. Just this morning I was doing Pilates and I became aware of the story in my head. *It's so early. I'm so tired. This hurts. I don't want to do this. This is hard,* was the general plot of my story. Some of this felt true, I'll admit to that. But I *did* want to be doing Pilates or I wouldn't have woken up and gone to the gym. I immediately changed my story to *This is difficult, not impossible. "Difficult" is just a thought you are having. Don't give up on yourself. Don't abandon yourself so easily.* Immediately I felt more inspired—and I finished the set.

The story we tell ourselves about who we are—our worth, how life works for us, our patterns, and our view of the world—defines how we see ourselves and how we act in our day-to-day lives. The stories we are attached to have enormous influence on the lenses through which we see the world, so it is important that we are telling stories where we like the ending.

Have you ever heard someone casually say . . .

- "I never catch a break."
- "Things just never go my way."
- "It's always something."
- "Just my luck" (when something bad happens).

This type of thinking sets you up to feel helpless and identify as being a victim to your circumstance. Being helpless is one of the worst and most shameful feelings a human can feel. We all fall prey to this kind of self-talk. The point here isn't to beat ourselves up for telling these stories, but rather to become aware of them so we can start to tell a better story that is more aligned with love.

You can rewrite the narrative and create a story that supports your growth. For example, if you identify with the thoughts above, try adding an opposite thought to give your narrative more balance. Eventually one day you will feel hopeful enough to just focus on what you want, but until then, balance is a good place to start.

- "I never catch a break" becomes "Sometimes I catch a break, and sometimes I don't. Life is all about experiencing contrast."
- "Things just never go my way" becomes "I win some and I lose some. Life isn't linear."
- "It's always something" becomes "Sometimes shit happens, sometimes it's terrible, and sometimes it's amazing."
- "Just my luck" becomes "This bad thing just happened. It has nothing to do with me personally, it just is what it is." (In other words, decrease your identification with bad things happening.)

Decide today to believe in the possibility of living from a new story. Live from the story where you are the hero (or shero, as I like to call it), because that is the story you were born to live.

3. Run toward Your Goal, Not away from Shame

We as women have such a long history with feeling second fiddle, less than, and unworthy. Our marginalized roles in society have left a long legacy of low self-worth and low self-esteem. Historically, and unfortunately still today, our bodies are subject to scrutiny and are considered objects to be made pleasant for others' visual and physical consumption. We've been long seen as arm candy and mere decoration.

This legacy lends itself to the deep feelings of shame that many women experience when they begin dieting. It is connected to the collective belief that our bodies must look a certain way in order for us to earn our place amongst our people. Any kind of association with this shame is going to eat away at our self-worth and will not benefit us on any level.

When you are working to change the Shame-Based Mindset, focus instead on what you are seeking, not on any residual feelings of shame or what you want to run away from. The questions below are meant to help you get clear on what you want to bring into your life (as opposed to what you are afraid of and running from). Getting clarity on our deeper "why" is critical for establishing long-term motivation for sustained behavior change.

- Why do you desire to feel good in your body?
- What exciting events in your future (travel, family activities, etc.) require you to be in a body that feels good and functions well?
- How will ending your battle with food positively change your life?
- Is there any health concern or pain that might improve if you changed your relationship with food?
- How would your relationships positively change if you had a more peaceful relationship with food?
- What could you be doing with your time and energy if you weren't always obsessing about food?
- How would changing your relationship with food affect your confidence?
- What do you want for yourself five years from today? Ten years from today?

We all carry some shame on some level. Remember, change is not linear, and the idea that you can eradicate all of your shame and start changing your relationship with food from a shame-free place overnight is just more of the old dichotomous thinking that got us here in the first place. It is okay to recognize feelings of shame; that makes you human. But you can choose, at all times, to focus on something better than the shame. You can see the shame for what it is—the old lie—and choose to run toward your new truth instead.

SUMMARY

1. Dieting and restriction from the traditional Shame-Based Mindset are predicated on the idea that you are unworthy in the body you occupy.
2. Any behavior predicated on shame is unable to provide positive outcomes, as it only serves to deepen the wound that is causing the unhappiness you feel in the first place.
3. The journey must feel like the destination.
4. You have the power to rewrite the narrative to tell yourself a better story about who you are.
5. You must move toward a goal that feels good, and avoid running from pain. Running from shame or pain only highlights the negative emotions, thus increasing your attention on the problem itself.

12

The Misdirected-Attention Mindset

Whatever we put our attention on will grow stronger in our life.

—Maharishi Mahesh Yogi

Diet Mindset #10: Misdirected-Attention Mindset
Type: Problem-Focused Mindset
Sounds Like: "I have a laundry list of foods I cannot eat, and yet all I can think about is food."
Cause: Dieting Focuses on Perceived Problems, Not Solutions

Let's talk about two crucial elements where change and human behavior are concerned: attention and intention.

Our intention is what we want to create when we set out into the day. It is our deepest "why." It is the outcome we set in our minds before we begin to create. It is literal, and although we are not always consciously aware of it, it is a driving force behind our desire.

Attention is simply what we place our mind on. It's what we watch and what we are mindful of. It is where our eyes, our mind, and our behavior is focused.

Our intention and attention are two of the most powerful tools we have available to us when it comes to change. They are miracle-working choices that are available for us to control at every turn in our lives. And yet, despite their amazing, life-changing abilities, many of us have never been told how to harness their power, and therefore we are running around wasting these very precious resources.

Worse yet, many of us are using our intention and attention to our disadvantage without even realizing it! Let me explain. What we place our attention on grows stronger. How many people go about trying to make personal changes by first focusing on all the things that are going wrong in their lives? It makes sense. I mean, how can we know what we want to change without identifying what isn't working?

The problem is that we miss a critical step in the change process (which I am going to teach you how to implement later in the chapter) and continue to focus on all of these "problems" while trying to change them. It never works. It's a misuse of our attention.

Let's use the example of someone on a diet.

Allison knows she wants a more balanced relationship with food. This is her intention. She has struggled with yo-yo dieting her whole life and feels tried and worn down by the constant food obsession and fear of weight gain. She is tired of always struggling with food and just wants to feel comfortable in her skin.

And so she sets a goal that she genuinely thinks is helpful, but due to social norms, is erred from the start. She probably makes a goal that sounds like this:

"I'm going to lose weight."

Here's the first thing to realize about why so many of us are unknowingly working against ourselves: the brain only focuses on the subject of message. What the brain is focusing on is simply WEIGHT!

It's the same thing if you state, "I don't want to be overweight." The brain is only paying attention to the subject, and it might as well be like the adult in a Charlie Brown cartoon. The brain is simply hearing:

"Blah, blah, blah, blah, blah, OVERWEIGHT."

Most people, when desiring to find balance with food, unwittingly end up focusing on the wrong things. They put their attention on the number they see on the scale now (instead of how they desire to feel—remember the lesson from chapter 11, the journey must feel the way we want the destination to feel?). They obsess over all the foods they "shouldn't" eat. They count endless calories and treat food as though it is an enemy. They put their attention on all the things they have been taught to fear (weight, "bad food," etc.) and are therefore trying to eliminate. This unknowingly guarantees that these very things will become the focus of their mind, possibly an obsession, and likely show up more and more in their experience as a result.

Don't believe me?

DO NOT THINK OF A WHITE BEAR!

Okay, so tell me what you just thought of? Despite my clear direction NOT to think of it, the brain conjured up an image of a white bear, no? We did this earlier in the book with the pink elephant, and it works the exact same way. Even though my earlier use of this tactic might have prepared you, your brain still thought of a white bear. It shows you that there isn't a way to override what I'm explaining.

This is why we drive ourselves insane on diets. All day we are saying, "Don't eat this" and "Don't eat that," and all we can think about is the food we are trying to steer clear of. It's maddening!

Remember, what we put our attention on grows in our lives. Your attention is precious because it's highly powerful in its ability to create realities. Be careful what you give your attention to, and remember how powerfully you are creating your reality simply by giving attention to certain thoughts and feelings.

Whatever you give attention to starts condensing into a reality in your life. Make sure your intentions and attention are focused on what you want more of in your life rather than focusing on erroneous cultural beliefs about your body that cause you to feel unworthy.

ACTION STEPS

1. *Focus on the Outcome Instead of the Problem*

The good news is, with the Misdirected-Attention Mindset, you can use what you have discovered is the problem to make a very simple solution. This goes nicely with the lesson in chapter 11 about chasing your motivation instead of running from pain. As you move forward, it is critical that you create clarity on what it is you really want in your life, as opposed to what you are trying to eliminate.

Earlier in the book, you began the process of exploring what your deeper, emotionally charged motivation was for desiring a new relationship with food. Build on what you discovered in the previous chapters to create clear intentions that will become your focal points for your attention from now on.

Daily, it is up to you to create intentional focus on the positive aspects you desire to bring into your life. Are you excited about finally releasing the struggle with food and body image? Focus on the excitement you feel having made that choice. (And do not let go of that focus. Like a dog with his favorite bone, it is your job to keep your attention on that feeling.)

Are you proud of your choice to introduce fresh, whole foods into your life, foods that nourish your body and help it thrive? Focus on that feeling of pride, and the meaning that it has for you in the evolution of your relationship with how you treat your body.

Do you want to feel strong and limber in your body? Focus on being strong and the movement and activity that makes you feel this way.

Have you decided to stop dieting, start eating mindfully, and accept where your body goes as a result? Then focus your intention on feeling acceptance and peace.

Do you want to feel light and free, both in your life and your body? Then focus on what you think levity and freedom feel like, and then make choices that align with that feeling of levity and freedom.

2. Try a Day Free of Complaints

Our thoughts and words have tremendous power. This is why it is so important that we take responsibility for what we are thinking and saying. Energy flows where attention goes. What are you putting your attention on?

Imagine what it would be like if you could go through a day and not complain, criticize, judge, or whine. What do you think you would do instead? Where do you think you would put your attention? How would you see the world and your circumstances if the above options (complaining, criticizing, judging, or whining) were not available?

Here's the thing: we all fall prey to negative thinking. At times I think negative thinking is even more acceptable and culturally supported than being optimistic and positive (depending on the circumstances). Think about how common it is when you ask someone how they are doing for their response to be "Oh, fine," or something like, "You know, getting by." Think about what people say when you ask about their job. You usually hear something like, "It's a paycheck" or "Just hanging on until Friday."

I could give a million more examples, but my point is that it is more common to hear people complain than it is to hear, "I am alive—I am feeling pretty good" or "I love my life, thanks for asking!"

I am well aware that we all have pain and struggle in life. No one is able to avoid that, nor should we try. It's important that we always acknowledge our feelings, whether we judge them as good or bad. So please don't hear this as my Pollyanna attempt to try to pump you full of rainbows and unicorns, because that's just not my style. It's normal, necessary, and balanced to feel your painful emotions. But how do you respond to them? What do you say and think? Believe me, I know how easy it is to get sucked into the quicksand of "complaint energy," and I know how it feels—disempowering and awful!

I also know how it feels to take ownership of your thoughts and choose to avoid complaining. It's possible to feel your feelings and not identify with them or act from them. It's your power in the face of anything life hands you. It's internal control, and ultimately it is an act of self-love to choose gratitude over grumbling.

It is important to note here that this action step is in no way encouraging people to look the other way in the face of things that are unfair or wrong. I've heard it said before that gratitude lists are a function of privilege, and while I see the point being made, I don't entirely agree. Oppression and wrongdoings in our world are issues that I believe must be brought into the light and faced head on. I just feel that the most empowered way to face anything is from the clarity of your intention and your desire. Focusing on the pain and the problem puts you in alignment with the low energy and nasty feelings associated with the issue you have the problem with. While at times motivating ("hell hath no fury like a woman scorned" type of motivation), aligning with this energy does not help you to understand yourself, your power, or your choice from a place of deep connection. Go ahead, get pissed. Be mad. There are plenty of things in our world to rage against. But before you create, be sure to shift your attention from the problem to what you want to create. We want to be connected with *our truth* when we create, lest we erroneously create more of the same problem we are fighting against because we unconsciously are aligning with the negative energy from which the problem was born. Mother Theresa is famous for saying once, "I was once asked why I don't participate in anti-war demonstrations. I said that I will never do that, but as soon as you have a pro-peace rally, I'll be there." In that statement, she makes my point.

So, if you are up for it, just for one day, see if you can challenge yourself to avoid complaining, criticizing, judging, or whining. And when you catch yourself in the act, just be kind and reframe what you said and find a different way to look at it. This exercise isn't about being perfect (spoiler alert: it's likely you will catch yourself complaining at some point). Perfection doesn't exist, and (as I hope you are learning by now in the book) it's part of the old Diet Mindset.

This exercise, and trying to avoid complaining in general, is about being very intentional and paying attention to your mindset. The exercise itself wakes you up to what is happening in your mind. When we refuse to give in to complaint energy, we are awakened to the messages within our pain. We are available to learn from the experiences instead of drown in the feelings they create. Our opportunity here is to be awake and feel our feelings without attaching to them. This gives us the ability to see the wisdom in the moment without losing our internal sense of authority over our choices in the moment.

You can't always choose your feelings, and you can't always choose all of your thoughts. But you can choose how you want to respond.

3. Practice Body and Food Gratitude

Don't roll your eyes. I know, gratitude is a very heavily used word these days. A buzz word, to say the least, and as is the case with similar well-worn words, people have a tendency to get tired of hearing about it. But don't dismiss it too soon. Remember, typically ideas become buzz words for a reason.

Gratitude is a powerful mindset shift that helps us see our lives through the eyes of love. So, for all of us self-love warriors, gratitude is one of our superpowers. When we make the choice to look at what is present and that which we are grateful for, we choose love. When we choose to focus on what we have instead of what is missing, we choose love.

Gratitude is our internal superpower that we have access to at all times. If you have practiced choosing gratitude, then you know what I'm talking about. It can change your perspective and mood in the moment. It alters your world.

There is always something to be grateful for, no matter how bad things are. This is not about denying your own struggles, or feeling as though you don't have the right to feel your feelings. This is about choosing to be focused on what is present, instead of seeing what is not present. (Sound familiar?)

Wayne Dyer has a quote that I often call upon when I need to reframe my thinking. He simply stated, "You can choose peace instead of this." It's sometimes this simple. You can choose to see your blessing in any situation, which can bring you peace.

With food and body image, there is always something to be grateful for. If we are going to shed the old Diet Mindset and reclaim our rightful relationship with food that is free of constraints and shame, we must consciously teach our mind to see the joy and beauty in that relationship. Gratitude does this.

In correlation to healing your relationship with food and body image, choosing to practice daily gratitude for the food you eat helps to heal the damaged relationship with food that dieting creates. So many of us see food as the enemy. By encouraging gratitude for the food we eat, we can begin to change that fear-based relationship and reclaim our natural relationship with food as a source of sustenance and pleasure.

The same can be said of body image. When we have many years of body hatred under our belt, feeling gratitude for our body can feel like a difficult task. Start small, and find one function of your body that you appreciate. It could be the legs that get you around, the brain that gives you choice, the eyes that are reading these words right now. Try to choose something new each day and expand on your gratitude. When you are more seasoned, challenge yourself to start to include elements of gratitude that include the body's esthetic, such as loving your hair or the color of your eyes.

Gratitude, like self-love discussed earlier in the book, is a daily commitment. It is a daily choice, and it is also a practice that is imperfect. But despite all of this, the rewards far outweigh the effort involved. Choose gratitude; choose self-love. They are one and the same.

SUMMARY

1. When you are dieting from the traditional Misdirected-Attention Mindset, you are focused on the problem, thus focusing your brain on the very thing you are trying to stop thinking about and operating from.
2. You must instead focus on the goal or outcome in order to begin teaching your brain the new way of thinking that is aligned with the solution.
3. You have the power to focus your thoughts and place your attention and intention on the desired outcome, but it requires that you stay mindful and redirect your thoughts on a continual basis. Avoiding negative thought patterns (such as complaining) and focusing on things you feel gratitude for help you do this.

13

Considerations

So there you have them, the Ten destructive Diet Mindsets that have been holding you back and causing your every effort to create a balanced and long-lasting healthy relationship with food to self-destruct. Are you ready to go out, change your mind, and change your life?

Well, hold on. Just one second.

Before you do, I have a few more things I want to make sure I share with you. These concepts and behaviors stem from the diet culture and are important things to mention to anyone who is interested in healing their relationship with food.

NUMBERS

Be careful of numbers as you relate to food and your body. It sounds strange, I know, but it's common knowledge in the eating-disorder world, and for good reason. When people are in treatment for eating disorders, they cannot use numbers when they talk in therapy or group. It's that important to try and let go of them. Let me explain why.

Numbers themselves are not inherently the problem. It is just that numbers, because they are finite, have a tendency to become symbols of linear progress that people project their self-worth onto. They are often seen in obsessions and compulsions, and people easily attach meaning to them.

Think about how often they show up in weight loss:

- Number on the scale
- Clothing size
- Calorie counting
- Food weighing
- Point tracking
- Exercise tracking (number of reps, steps, or miles)
- Progress tracking (number of days on a diet, exercise plan, etc.)

All of these numbers aren't really anything other than a data point with regard to a measure we are seeking to understand, but they become an external measure of our worth. Most of us have succumbed to losing our entire day to the wrong number on the scale or the feeling of defeat when we no longer fit into a certain size pants.

So, generally speaking, I recommend that you not fixate on numbers. I do not encourage people to track calories or points for this reason. I find it a much gentler and sustainable practice to instead focus on hunger and fullness as a guide to the amount one should eat.

Remember, a number is external, and only our inner wisdom knows what we need. An example of this is in my former life of revolving diets, I tried a well-known diet that followed a point system. I always felt as though the points were off. Inevitably, I would be hungry on days I had no points left and not hungry on the days when I had excess points. Regardless of the fact that some of the points carried over, I never found that the points themselves ever aligned with what my body actually wanted or needed.

WEIGHING AND SCALES

As an eating-disorder therapist, my background and bias are largely against using scale weight as a measure of success when trying to create a healthier relationship with food. Most of my clients have come from an unhealthy background that is permeated with obsession around numbers (scale weight, calories, clothing sizes, food measurements, etc.). The scale is a tool, but for many people it has morphed way beyond a tool into this thing we step on that tells us if we are going to feel good or bad that day.

As was discussed in the book, whenever we give our power of discernment away to an external variable and allow some objective measure of "success" to define our own understanding of "good enough," we are creating a trap for ourselves.

Using scale weight is one of the easiest ways to fall into that trap. It is true that for some people, a weekly weigh-in allows them to keep track of how their eating is affecting their physical body. It is also true that for some people, they can do this in a sane and objective manner. But I find that, for a lot of women, this ability is more the exception than it is the rule.

For many women, stepping on a scale invites a daily or weekly ritual of allowing some number to define the mood they will be in that day, how they will feel in their body, and the thoughts they will think for the remainder of the day. It is too easy to fall into the trap of giving our power away to the almighty number on the scale. And as someone who is now dedicated to getting out of destructive Diet Mindsets, I encourage you to take caution with using any external measure of success that you have a toxic history with.

Check in with yourself and ask the following questions:

- Does counting calories make you feel crazy and kick in deprivation syndrome?
- Does weighing yourself determine how you feel in your skin?
- Does refusing to wear clothing in a certain dress size limit your wardrobe depending on what your body is doing that day?

If you have an unhealthy pattern, you will recognize it because it makes you feel bad. Choose instead ways of tracking your health and progress (nonlinear though it may be!) that you feel balanced with.

Can you work with a dietitian to help guide you and inform your choices as you begin to trust yourself with food again?

Can you do a daily check-in with your choices and your behaviors to bring mindful awareness to whether you are aligning with your true desires?

Can you use your energy levels and physical strength as a way of determining if you feel healthy and vibrant or sluggish and dull?

Notice that all of these suggestions above are subjective measures of outcome, not objective ones. Unlike numbers, these measures look to you for the answer as opposed to using something external. This reinforces the self-reference for authority and also reinforces trusting yourself to make decisions about your self-care.

Bottom line, if the scale (and the numbers) in any way sets you back into the old Diet Mindset, it isn't your friend. There are other ways to stay healthy and mindful of your body's needs.

BODY POSITIVITY

There is a movement afoot, and it's worth looking at. The Body Positivity Movement has many factions and branches, so for the sake of this book I am simply going to give a general overview.

The Body Positivity Movement is a movement that encourages people to adopt more respectful, forgiving, and positive attitudes toward their bodies, with the goal of improving self-esteem and well-being. This movement can be seen actively in social media. I encourage you to Google "body positive movement" and follow some body-positive bloggers and Instagram and Facebook accounts.

Why am I mentioning this movement? I do so because it offers a new voice that counters the beliefs of the negative Diet Mindsets. The movement exists, and although it is nowhere near as big as the cultural norm of thin-seeking perfectionism, it is growing daily and is worth exploring.

If you have been dieting or restricting most of your life, the concepts being touted as truth in the Body Positivity Movement are going to challenge your old way of thinking, but maybe that's a good thing. If you live in a larger body and want to work on learning to love and accept yourself and improve your self-esteem, linking to a community where your body is already accepted as beautiful, regardless of your desire to change or not change, is a deeply healing and empowering thing, and something our culture is dearly lacking.

If you want to continue to stretch your mind and move away from the Diet Mindset, I truly encourage you to get curious and explore this movement. There are many inspiring and courageous women out there creating a new narrative about what it means to be a woman in our world, and the role our bodies play in our overall worth. Hearing new and inspired messages will only help to reinforce the changes you will make as you change your mindsets, and finally, heal and reclaim your relationship with food.

GOING FORWARD

The bottom line to all of this is that dieting with a negative Diet Mindset is a destructive process that, while often well intended, can lead to serious emotional and psychological pain. The good news is we can be happy and healthy and not abandon ourselves in the process. We can eat without obsession and we can enjoy our lives without always thinking about food and our weight.

You have taken the first steps toward getting off a diet and changing the way you think—changing your mindset. This is the beginning of moving away from the agony and self-sabotage of dieting and toward a more aware and mindful relationship with food, and with yourself.

Your journey is just starting, so I hope you are excited about the changes that are coming sooner than you realize. Once you realize which destructive Diet Mindsets have been sabotaging you and keeping you stuck in the struggle, you can actively begin to reverse them by changing your thoughts and enacting the action steps presented in the previous chapters.

When I was a little girl, I remember being mesmerized by *The Wizard of Oz*. It was both magical and frightening. One of my favorite scenes from the movie is when Dorothy finally realizes that she always contained the answers, both in what she was initially seeking and how to find her way home once she got lost.

This is such a wonderful analogy and a perfect summary for the underlying message in this book. You were born with a healthy and balanced relationship with food. Somewhere along the way, through no fault of your own, you were misled and misguided by dieting and our unhealthy cultural beliefs about food and body image.

You found yourself lost, much like Dorothy. In order to find your way home, you continually sought out some external authority (like the Wizard) until you finally realized that there is no such thing! Hallelujah! You've learned the truth. Dieting does not work!

Much like Dorothy unveiling the Wizard's identity to find nothing more than an ordinary man behind the curtain, when we break through the core of dieting and reveal the truth about Diet Mindsets, it is clear that there are no experts coming to save us. We must realize what Dorothy realized toward the end of the film: In order to find our way home—and reclaim the healthy relationship with food that we were born with and that is our inherent right—all we have to do is realize that the answers and the power have always been inside of us.

> *You've always had the power, my dear. You just had to learn it for yourself.*
>
> —Glinda the Good Witch, *The Wizard of Oz*

Resources

Eating Disorders and Body Image

- Creative Health Initiatives (CHI), www.creativehealthinitiatitves.com
- Gurze Books, www.gurzebooks.com
- International Association of Eating Disorders Professionals (IAEDP), iaedp.com
- Something Fishy, www.something-fishy.org
- National Eating Disorders Association, www.nationaleatingdisorders.org
    - Online Screening, www.nationaleatingdisorders.org/online-eating-disorder-screening
- Caring Online, www.caringonline.com
- Overcoming Overeating, www.overcomingovereating.com
- National Association of Anorexia Nervosa and Associated Disorders, www.anad.org
- The Body Positive Project, www.thebodypositive.org
- Light Of the Moon Café (online courses for transforming your relationship with food), lightofthemooncafe.com

General Mental Health

- National Alliance on Mental Illness, www.nami.org

- Mental Health America, www.mentalhealthamerica.net
- National Institute of Mental Health, www.nimh.nih.gov
- PsychCentral, www.psychcentral.com

Dialectical Behavioral Therapy (DBT) Websites

- Behavioral Tech, www.behavioraltech.com
- DBT Peer Connections, www.ilovedbt.com
- DBT Self Help, www.dbtselfhelp.com
- Radically Open, www.radicallyopen.net

Assistance in Finding a Therapist or Dietitian

- Psychology Today Therapist Finder, therapists.psychologytoday.com
- International Association of Eating Disorders Professionals (IAEDP), iaedp.com

Additional Books

- *Eating in the Light of the Moon*, Anita Johnston, PhD
- *Intuitive Eating*, Evelyn Tribole, MS, RD, and Elyse Resch, MS, RD, FADA
- *Health at Every Size*, Linda Bacon, PhD

References

Cuddy, Amy J. C., Caroline A. Wilmuth, and Dana R. Carney. "The Benefit of Power Posing Before a High-Stakes Social Evaluation." Harvard Business School Working Paper, No. 13-027, September 2012.

Garner, D. M. (1998). "The effects of starvation on behavior: Implications for dieting and eating disorders." *Healthy Weight Journal*, 12(5), 68–72.

Harris, R. (2016, July 20). "The Three Main Parts of Your Brain by Dr. Russ Harris" [Video file]. Retrieved from https://youtu.be/5CpRY9-MIHA.

Johnston, Anita. *Eating in the Light of the Moon: How Women Can Transform Their Relationship with Food through Myths, Metaphors, and Storytelling*. Place of publication not identified: Gurze, 2001.

Linehan, Marsha M. *Cognitive-Behavioral Treatment of Borderline Personality Disorder*. Enskede: TPB, 2008.

Siegel, D. (2012, February 29). "Dr. Dan Siegel presenting a Hand Model of the Brain" [Video file]. Retrieved from https://youtu.be/gm9CIJ74Oxw.

Williamson, Marianne. *A Return to Love: Reflections on the Principles of a Course in Miracles*. New York: HarperPerennial, 2012.

Wolfe, Naomi. *The Beauty Myth: How Images of Beauty Are Used Against Women*. Toronto: Vintage Books, 1990.

About the Author

Becca Clegg is a licensed professional counselor, certified eating-disorder specialist (CEDS), IAEDP-approved eating-disorder supervisor, and certified clinical hypnotherapist. She is the president and clinical director of Authentic Living, a psychotherapy practice specializing in the treatment of women in recovery from eating disorders and body-image issues. Becca is also the co-clinical director of Creative Health Initiatives (CHI), a group-therapy program that focuses on providing outpatient groups, programs, and workshops to women. In addition to her clinical practice, Becca is also a speaker, writer, and teacher, and presents nationally educating and facilitating workshops for women and other clinicians on the treatment of eating disorders, body image, and women's issues. For more information about Becca and her work, visit www.rebeccaclegg.com.